## About the Author

Ah, the bit where I give a page about... me. I'm from the little town of Andover in Hampshire and this is my first book of what I hope will be many more. I am an absolute rugby nut, whether it's watching it or still trying to play it through the aches and pains of entering my mid-thirties and an ever-expanding waistline! The rest of my spare time it's puzzles, cycling, camping and the great outdoors, but the thing I value most are the times I spend with my family and friends. So that's me, nothing else left to say other than enjoy the book, thank you.

# 8 Minutes 37 Seconds

# Craig Allan

# 8 minutes 37 seconds

Olympia Publishers
*London*

**www.olympiapublishers.com**
OLYMPIA PAPERBACK EDITION

A CIP catalogue record for this title is
available from the British Library.

ISBN: 978-1-78830-905-9

First Published in 2021

Olympia Publishers
Tallis House
2 Tallis Street
London
EC4Y 0AB

Printed in Great Britain

# Dedication

This book is dedicated to Ian 'Ianado!' Runciman — Win, lose or draw, I finished it, mate, thank you.

# 8:37.36

Sounds either naff or intriguing, doesn't it? Choosing a time for a title. Was that how much time I have left to save the world? No. Was it how long was left to climb to the top of the tallest skyscraper and disarm the nuclear bomb, getting to be the hero for once? Nope. Was it how much time I have left on the clock to save the girl of my dreams from impending doom before we rode off into the sunset together in my heavily rusted, twenty-year-old two-seater convertible? Or was it some sort of Olympic record I set through battling all odds? Unfortunately, not.

Sorry… the truth is a lot less exhilarating than all those things, I'm afraid, but it is important.

The time of 8:37.36 is the moment I freeze my stopwatch in the dirty, unkempt, work toilet cubicle just after flushing the chain and right before I unhook the latch on the thin wooden door and begin to wash my hands. It also includes in its recording the time taken to travel to those facilities from the other side of the warehouse, which takes up about a minute of that recording, it's also the time I spent washing my hands quickly before using the facilities and the time taken to select what was the cleanest cubicle out of the four disgusting, horrible crap traps available to me, which was actually quite a difficult task where I work, as normally every seat possessed the remains of an unwashed and untrained middle-aged welder's butt smear on the back of the seat like they were never taught to clean their arses properly.

Once the cubicle had been carefully selected and under time pressure, I also recorded within the data the time taken to sanitise the selected cubicle with wipes and a small bottle of alcohol gel which I supplied myself as the cleaners were non-existent and then go about my business. It sounds silly, doesn't it? Ridiculous, in fact, why on earth would I record my own toilet times at work? Well, I assure you it's not a weird fetish that has developed over my working life — short answer is I have to do it.

Everything I divulge to you in this book is the absolute truth and is as accurate as I can tell you. I have changed names, hidden company names and dates of events. Even my own identity has been kept from these pages because quite simply I don't want to be caught up in any libel or defamation cases. Even if I was well within my right to give out such details, I would be what I called dead right in those circumstances. Meaning no matter how much the law may be on my side because I'm telling the truth, that alone wouldn't prevent it ending up in a defamation trial, I'm afraid, and I'd be right at the expense of my time, money and confrontation in some kind of courtroom, which I know very little about and that's the kind of right I want to avoid. I will let no one I write about in this book have their say or provide them with any opportunity to lie or spin their way out of what I have written, which is what they'd inevitably do; they're good at it. After years of abuse and mismanagement and knowingly doing so, they have lost their opportunity to challenge my words. They don't deserve it and they'd be too spineless to accept any responsibility for what they did. What's important in all of this is the 'what'. The message, the stories and the moments themselves. What has happened, what is still happening today and what we can all learn from it. Names and places will be a sure-fire way to complicate the matter, both legally and in terms of blurring the message; it's not about the who. If I revealed who indeed is responsible for all of this, it's all you could get caught up on. It's about what happened and what is still happening, not just to me but to thousands, possibly tens of thousands of people up and down the country every day.

The time on my stopwatch represents a type of oppression in its newest form. It represents unnecessary stress and unnecessary challenging, it represents technicality used for exploitation in employment law and an open door for bullying and torment. It represents a cold truth of how little we are actually protected by the laws that govern us in the workplace and leave us all wide open to harassment and unfair profiteering by those among us willing to be so ruthless.

It's one of many examples that is making work in this country more and more unbearable, particularly in the unskilled sector, yet it is never talked about.

With more businesses having to economise in the next few years I can only see these types of situations increasing and getting worse.

You see, I had to start recording the times that I went to the toilet and write them down on a piece of scrap paper that I carried around with me in my pocket because my grotesque line leader was beginning to pull me up over the frequency and time spent on these visits. Telling me the number of times I was visiting was unacceptable despite the fact he could never actually tell me how often I was going or how long I was spending in there. It was twice a day (a pee taking considerably less time by the way), and believe me, I'd rather hold it in if I could then not be subjected to that bacteria-infested shit pit I had to call a toilet more than I had to. The company's third-rate, overpriced coffee pumping through the unkempt machine's pipes pretty much made it an unavoidable issue.

I would explain to him constantly that I only went twice a day, but he ignored it, dismissed it, or accused me of lying to him. He was calling me up on it every visit and doing it very vocally to the point that I had to ask a colleague to start making a note of the number of times I went each day so the next time he challenged me, and he did, I'd have the evidence to shoot down his pathetic and pointless accusation. After my colleague had assisted me, I thought that would be an end to that little drama, but it wasn't. He then began questioning the amount of time I was spending in there upon each visit, ten, fifteen minutes I was accused of each time. He could never prove any of this, of course, he was just being a bully, so the onus fell on me to have to disprove once again his unsubstantiated claim. I phoned an independent legal advice line on employment law only for them to tell me that what he was doing technically wasn't illegal regardless of how highly unethical it may have been; there was no law to prevent him from questioning me or interrogating me.

I was left with no choice but to buy myself a stopwatch, that's right, a stopwatch to time myself defecating. A thirty-year-old man having to record his toilet times just so he could have the upper hand in arguments regarding his toilet use which he should never have been subjected to in the first place. The bosses didn't have the time to focus on the fact the toilets were always filthy, used by people whose parents avoided basic potty training or that I always achieved my targets and over, no, the most important issue was the manager thought she may have seen me use the toilet a little too often and my supervisor was straight on it.

He could have defended me to her, put the issue to bed or even addressed it as being a purely ridiculous notion to have to micro-manage, "I don't think so" or "What's the problem? It's not affecting his work or targets!", but that, of course, would have required some sort of backbone and given his jellyfish-like exterior I doubt seriously he possessed one. It was easier for him to come down heavy on a hardworking, average-paid thirty-year-old man on how he excessively used the work toilet even though he didn't!

I had to buy the stopwatch to prove my argument; it was an accurate way of recording my time spent in there but buying it didn't stop the argument itself. It just proved I was right within it; the bullying and harassment continued; the damage was done. The stopwatch could never return a measure of peace to me in my job at the bottom of the working pile. Holding that clock in my hand every time was a reminder that I had to fight tooth and nail just to keep a low-end job that I didn't like but possibly could have under different circumstances.

I could have changed jobs and taken my chances elsewhere and hoped my new employers were better. I could have escalated it and taken it to the management but that was a pointless task as it was them that set that dog onto me in the first place.

I could have raised it with HR but even if I was lucky enough to get a member of that team that wasn't in the manager's "click", they weren't breaking any laws.

I could have sought help externally and say I was being

harassed, well, that's a fine option, sure, if I had the money or savings to pay the legal fees, but I didn't. I was bottom of the pile earning which meant at best if I was really good with my money, I could live from month to month without having to borrow off my family, and that's before I could even start worrying about whether I could prove it or not.

I could have taken the case on myself, spent every spare moment I had of my own time dedicating myself to understanding employment law, pursuing a case which had a very flexible and loose standing point but would have achieved very little because in the eyes of the law they weren't doing anything wrong.

All avenues, no matter how much I was entitled to them, lacked any resolution, each 'right' I had on paper was essentially a dead end in reality.

My problems would never be resolved. I would go through stress, time, money, even having to seek new employment for nothing.

It's not just toilet breaks that are being squeezed, pressured or changed by businesses, it's every conceivable thing an idiot devoid of empathy can think of from getting a cup of water to hot drinks, from break times to holiday requests.

Protection by employment law in this country appears to me to be the work of a good con man. We're led to believe we are safe and secure in our places of work from exploitation or harassment or unfair treatment but it's just an illusion, an illusion more and more employers are beginning to see through. Once they know how the trick is done and how little the consequences can impact them, they start to harass and bully those that don't fit in to their ever-changing environments.

08:37.36 reminds me there is no such thing as a simple nine to five any more. You can't just go to a job, keep your head down, work hard and go home. You have to dance to their tune, let yourself go completely to their song and show you are willing to bend as much as they ask while they strip back your break times to the bare minimum, give you the worst jobs in the place hoping it breaks you, tell you when you can take your holiday even when it doesn't fulfil a business need, question your toilet breaks, question you every time you get a cup of water, question your conduct repeatedly, hound you and harass you in situations they know can never be proven and even break the law, knowing it's a mountain to climb emotionally and financially for most of us just to attempt to restore a balance.

I hope you will find the coming pages an interesting journey where you can get a taste of modern working conditions in certain businesses and get to know what exactly is happening and being expected of our future generations entering the workplace. More importantly, I hope to try and tackle these rapidly growing issues with possible solutions and explain what we can do to try and combat these problems effectively so we can create a better working environment for everybody. Lastly, I will explain why I think this is all happening.

Thank you and I hope you enjoy.

# Chapter One
# Building up

It was a Wednesday afternoon. The rain was pounding down on the ageing tin warehouse roof. Its ferociousness overpowered the cheap second-hand radio that blared out across the building, which wasn't a bad thing. It was the same local radio station we had on every day with the exact same playlist; the managers insisted on only having one station. The ever-present sweet smell from the cardboard and packaging that travelled throughout the place hit my nostrils. The dust and particles from their distribution slowly built up, blocking my airways as the day wears on.

I was slumped over a tall, blue, heavy, four-foot steel rack on wheels, used to store all the finished items of the living aid products we built, watching three other guys working. I'd been watching them every day for the past four weeks and I was fed up. Really fed up. Like suddenly on that day I'd found rock bottom in my mental capacity to maintain the crummy existence I found myself in. I'd had enough. Enough of Life, enough of the stupid rules, enough of all the absolute crap I had to take just to earn a few quid.

There were visions beginning to play out in my head where I am screaming out at the top of my voice, ripping and tearing my vocal cords to the point that my throat is swelling and closing up. I'm tearing away all the standardised work uniform from my clammy, overworked body as I enter into pure, beautiful rage and begin pulling all the storage racks over on each production line in every part of the building. I'm enjoying watching every item break and smash apart as they're driven into the grey painted concrete floor. I then start throwing and launching tools across the warehouse hoping they damage something in their flight path and then I am taking every nut, every bolt and every washer stored in all those tiny little pathetic plastic trays on each line and pouring them all into a big pile in the middle of the warehouse. I run up and drive my steel toe through the base of that metal pile, kicking the metal components everywhere precariously and watching them fall like metal confetti, while I take joy from the fact I'm destroying their business. I want to put holes in every fake partition, every office wall, pull down every sign, every company and corporate poster that bears a false message selling a concept rather than the truth. I felt like smashing desks up into tiny bits of wood, breaking windows and throwing computers. I wanted to cause nothing but absolute destruction while my colleagues watched and opened their eyes and began breaking their chains of conformity to join in the chaos. I wanted mayhem while my managers and supervisors looked on, jaws dropped, not knowing what to do because the management training they lived and died by didn't quite cover the events unfolding in front of them. I wished to tear the company apart, because I hated what they represented. I hated the lies, intimidation and manipulation and I hated how they treated their staff. The lack of respect or dignity given to hard workers wanting an honest life felt untenable. I despised the false image they fed on to sell their cheap, tatty and overpriced garbage while breaking the law to do it. I wanted to change the whole world with my rage and frustration as it grew and grew and showed no sign of stopping or being tamed by reason. I wanted to use my anger as a reset button for all the crap going on all over this planet, like the down treading of the masses to line the pockets of the few and the ongoing deceit we're forced to swallow. I had the strongest desire to make a stand and show the world how things should be done, make a better world for everybody, by sheer blunt force, generated by the years of frustration and torment.

I didn't act on these feelings, of course, and I was never going to. I knew no matter how angry I got or how much I destroyed the warehouse, the world wouldn't just change. It was nothing but a ridiculous fantasy. The company would survive regardless of any damage I caused it, they'd lose a day's production at best. My colleagues wouldn't have broken from their chains of conformity and joined in the chaos to fight for a fairer world because the managers and supervisors would have probably laughed at the sight of one of their biggest problems finally having a meltdown right in front of them. I'd have been arrested for destruction of private and company property. I'd probably have received a fine and/or prison sentence, giving me a permanent criminal record and making me practically unemployable for any other shitty dead-end job for the rest of my working life. I'd also have certainly created some gossip for the other production operatives for a couple weeks at the vending machine, whilst they purchased their overpriced, third-rate coffees (at least until the next hot topic came along).

Why rock bottom? Why that day?

I was a production operative, or to put it plainly, I was a factory worker which has got to be hands down the world's most boring occupation, and I was also a trainer. What that means is I'd work the build lines with the other guys, same hours, same pay, but I'd also get paid to train new temps when they came in for an extra twenty pounds a week and to some this was seen as a promotion. Hitting the big time with their extra fifty pence an hour but I never took it too seriously, well, the position bit of it, I was no higher up than anyone else, it was like being made a team captain or a prefect; you took on the crap the real higher ups never wanted to do and you got nothing for it except to call yourself a little higher up, which you really weren't, like being able to proudly call yourself chief gimp. None of the work was rocket science. I could do most of it in my sleep.

As part of the training role, once you've instructed them on how to build the product you have to oversee their work and quality check all the builds coming through. Put simply, I'm paid a little extra to stand behind the newbies on the back of a line and watch them work. Sounds easy enough, doesn't it? Well, let me tell you, after about forty minutes it's like having your soul slowly eaten away. There was a large digital clock always in my line of sight mounted high up on the wall and I couldn't help but watch the minutes slowly tick by. After a day or two of training the fresh batch, when no more mistakes were coming through it always gave me time to think, way too much time. On that particular Wednesday the thoughts were dark, negative and very real. On that day I decided I hated the whole Western working world, the world I was living in and I hated what it stood for. I hated every company that made money through deceit, selling their brands with the utmost professional image of a smiling model on a pricey advert, telling you how amazing their product was and how perfect the company was knowing they were selling you complete crap or an image rather than the product itself. I hated knowing that so many people took this crap on face value and never scratched beneath the surface to find the truth because the truth was too inconvenient for them. The truth being these companies treat their staff like something they've stepped in, but who wants morality hanging over a purchase these days? They may not have necessarily been breaking any laws, but they were getting away with providing the bare minimum to staff and customers alike, and taking everything they could while promising a standard of excellence to and for everyone. Constantly treading a fine legal line and asking their workforce to leave dignity and self-respect at the clocking-in machine to carry out their dirty deeds for them.

I hated that I worked as hard as I did, in a job I didn't like for so long and had very little to show for it. Of course, I knew I wasn't in the minority on this. "That's life!", so I'm always told. Is it though, really? The real point of having a job and working hard to make someone else rich is that you also get to improve your standard of living a little along the way, but the concept is dying. Inflation is forever rising, the hourly rates or minimum wages are not increasing in line with inflation and if companies are already paying above minimum, they are reluctant to increase their wages at all. Whenever a company tells you they have to tighten their belts, what it really means is that they're going to be tightening yours. Rent is constantly on the increase too! With landlords basically charging whatever they like with minimal government policing and don't even bother going to your local council for housing any more, unless you want to be laughed out the door or you've got seventeen kids and are prepared to share a three-bed house.

It seems that these days nearly every council is stretched to breaking point with waiting lists and will rely on private landlords to provide extra housing at whatever the landlord decides to charge. This means they can't even support those in need, let alone those actually earning a living but can't afford to go private and don't earn enough to buy.

Every product we buy, every bit of food purchased in the supermarket, every time we buy a new pair of shoes it's all becoming more and more expensive year on year. The value of what we earn is decreasing while prices continue to rise through taxation and maximizing profit.

Consequently, as a thirty-year-old man with no kids, no debt, no wife or girlfriend to take care of, my full-time job can only afford a rented room in a shared house, and after some careful shopping and a car to run, I'm not left with an awful lot to show for my hard work at the end of each month. That just isn't right or fair when I work as hard as I do and see so many others around me getting what appears to be a free ride.

"Well, why didn't you go to college and get some qualifications? Then you could earn more money and get a better job."

To those who would throw this ridiculous question my way, I would simply burst your bubble by saying that I was brought up in a place of responsibility rather than choice. I helped my family from a young age by bringing money into the house and as much as you may have lucked out with your circumstances, do not assume everyone else is afforded those same choices because that's just not reality. I had to work; there wasn't a choice. The few lucky and exceptional people have those choices and create those opportunities but those who don't possess the academic intellect to engage in further education but are still willing to work hard and contribute to our society should not be punished by a sub-standard way of living; they are still contributing in an honest and decent way. Also, let's not forget, higher education is no guarantee of employment once the qualifications have been obtained. More and more people are leaving college and universities drowning in debt, seeking work in small and competitive job markets and wondering how exactly they're going to apply their degree in dance.

I was so angry that day because I was looking at my life and thinking right, you have done everything society has asked of you. You've worked your butt off, paid your way in life, always been respectful, always stayed on the right side of the law, and what do you have to show for it? Nothing, nada, zilch. And I'm not asking for the world's smallest violins to be broken out and played for my sad story because let's face it, there's so many people in our country and all over the world in a worse situation than mine, a lot worse. I'm sure I'm not the only person that goes to work and asks themselves what it's all for, but one of the things that tipped me over the edge, to the near point of rage, was a conversation I'd had with a friend of mine the night before. He was a manager of one of the local pubs in town that was owned by one of the big breweries. We were out running early one evening around the lakes that back onto one of the town's council estates as we normally did a few times a week, only this particular evening, he seemed quieter than normal, so I asked him what was up.

He told me that he'd received an email from his area manger rolling out a new shift pattern for all his employees.

"Right. So what's the problem?" I asked him.

"Basically, what they're saying is, shift times will now be

starting and finishing fifteen minutes later," he said, stopping in the road to make eye contact with me.

"So? Doesn't seem that drastic. What's the big deal?" I replied.

"The reason that they're doing it is, say your shift pattern is five till close? Well, now your shift will be quarter past five till close. Chances are you'll more than likely turn up at around the same time as you normally would. Say five to five or ten to five, so you're not late. And you'll most likely stick to your same arrival routine." He paused. "So when you turn up early you'll intend to sit there at the bar or outside with your phone having a quick fag, until your shift begins. But if you go in and the pub is absolutely rammed with customers that want serving and your colleague or mates are struggling, most people will not just sit there and watch." He looked at me, to make sure I was following the gist. "You're going to jump behind the bar and lend a hand and it will be for free," he said,

"I wouldn't help out,'" I replied, shrugging my shoulders.

"You would!" he retorted. "Well, most people would, because guilt would get the better of them and if it didn't, at the very least it would certainly cause animosity amongst the workers you've left struggling there, drowning in customers, while you sit playing games on your phone."

"So you're telling me they've gone to all that effort of rolling out a new shift pattern countrywide with an adjustment of fifteen minutes, so they play people's guilt and emotions for the sake of a few quid?"

"It's not a few quid, though, is it? It's a couple of members of staff per pub per day across the entire country being stripped of quarter of an hour's pay per day. It's going to save them thousands and more than likely get the same standards of work anyway. They pretty much admitted the reason in the email. It's all about reducing staff costing!"

"So what about all the members of staff that they've upset across the company?"

He laughed at my question.

"Do you really think they'll care? You'll get a few that will leave because it's a step too far. Most will stay and moan about it for a while and after a few months it'll become the norm, or they'll refuse to come in any earlier and help and either risk being late or risk upsetting their colleagues because they sat there and did nothing. Brilliant, isn't it? The directors and group managers will all get a pat on the back and a nice little bonus and be told how wonderful they are for coming up with the idea. The pub manager will no doubt get an earful from his staff for having to roll out the new initiative and the poor teenage student trying to earn a few quid in a minimum wage job will risk getting a talking to from her colleagues if she doesn't help them for free before her start time."

"That's just disgusting. I can't believe people can be so ruthless!"

"That's the way the world works now, mate. Ordinary people have no value in business. If they quit, there's ten people ready and waiting in line, desperate to fill that spot and earn a wage, and they'll be willing to follow the rules in place as it's all new to them."

We left the conversation there and quickly moved onto other things. We finished our run and he dropped me home. As soon as he drove off up the road and out of sight, my thoughts quickly returned to what he'd said to me. I couldn't get it out of my head. All those people made unhappy and frustrated, emotionally blackmailed, all from an idea born from an idiot in a suit and tie hiding behind his laptop, eager to impress his superiors in any way he could think of to justify keeping his job a little longer, regardless of the cost to others. Not dismissing human emotion for the sake of business or any buzzwords floating around from his latest PowerPoint training but relying on it. Relying on the ties between those at the bottom to help their fellow worker for nothing while they lined their boss's pockets with a few extra pennies.

My poor girlfriend got the full force of my thoughts in a rant when I entered through the front door that evening. I explained the conversation, then went on about how bad I felt for the staff because they were clearly undervalued, how frustrated I felt at my friend's situation because he had to roll out this new change and if he didn't agree or refused to roll with it he could face the sack, and because he lived in the pub he would lose his home and his family's home in the process. So much to lose for the sake of one manager's protest that wouldn't amount to anything anyway, as the other thousands of managers across the country would be rolling it out without hesitation anyway. Just like the people my friend managed, he could be replaced so easily by a number of assistant managers ready to step up and make their mark at a moment's notice and carry out the change without a second thought. He was bent over a barrel.

I wasn't naive to this type of behaviour in the workplace. I was experiencing this kind of stuff myself and daily, but what I detested was how widespread it seemed to be, creeping into every different sector, steadily growing, infecting and changing the internal structure like a strong disease. I hated how matter of fact it all was that people and methods such as these existed like, "that's just life", "suck it up, get on with it".

Well no, sorry, but that sort of thing just doesn't sit with me. You ask someone to come in and work hard for your business, serve your food, your drinks at a fast pace, show constant professionalism and to always be polite even in the face of some very rude people, all for a minimum wage and that isn't enough. You want to strip away their peace of mind, put emotional pressure on all of them at the very start of each shift all for the sake of quarter of an hour's minimum wage. It seemed by the time I'd hit thirty, we were discovering, as a society, the very price of our morals and inconsideration towards others for little self-gain in our careers and lives and it was very cheap indeed. How could the genius behind this shift idea sleep at night? Answer is quite comfortably, I imagine. In a luxury bed paid for by a comfortable salary and generous bonus. I couldn't sleep. It had bothered me that much because like I said earlier, I was experiencing the same things in my job, but knowing it was everywhere made me realise it would get harder and harder to escape these kinds of environments as time went on. Time taken away out of our day, break times cut short, overtime rates cut, colleagues feeling overworked and undervalued, people sacked or let go for trivial reasons. It seemed as though everywhere I turned and every story I heard from friends and family, the people at the bottom were being dumped on.

The next morning, I woke up a little later than usual feeling very groggy having only grabbed three and a half hours of sleep. I made myself a strong coffee with lots of sugar and got ready for work. By that time, I really didn't like the mornings any more. The idea of going to work actually made me feel a little anxious and a bit sick each morning because it was no longer just a place to earn a wage for honest work.

Work was a battleground, a nightmare filled with petty politics constantly having to stand up and fight for every inch of your liberty that was being taken away by some truly awful human beings when all we wanted to do was just keep our heads down and get on with our jobs.

I parked up and reached the electronic clocking-in machine at 7:55. Work started at eight o'clock, exactly eight o'clock! I swiped my card and entered the warehouse. I figured there was ample time to get myself a cup of coffee from the canteen's poorly kept machine before I went on to the morning brief. There were two people queued in front of me at the machine, annoying but no big deal; it didn't take long at all to get to the machine. I still felt a little sluggish from the bad night's sleep, but I had my life-saving coffee in my hand so headed for the morning meeting. The morning meetings were always held in the same place every day, the centre of the warehouse right in the middle of all the production lines. There were three leaders that chaired the morning briefs and you'd find your respective group. The original idea of these gatherings was to read out which line you'd be working on that day, highlight any health and safety concerns to the leader and for them to read out any company news or updates as well as giving praise to staff or teams and feedback. Over the past eighteen months the meetings had gradually turned into a quick readout of where you were working and the rest of the time was an opportunity to tell you what you were doing wrong and hand out any new rules. No room or time left to praise those who worked hard or excelled in any areas of their job, no compliments, no motivation, no words of thanks or inspiration. Literally nothing positive was ever mentioned for well over a year and a half towards the staff. The leaders couldn't even muster a "have a good day", or "thank you". It became a matter of "here's what you're doing wrong. Now go away."

Because of my rushed but much needed coffee dash, I was the last one in the team to show up. I remember distinctly the clock had turned to 08:00 exactly as I walked up to the huddle. I was within three steps from the team, so there was no reason for me to worry. I'd timed it perfectly.

"Err right morning, everyone," that familiar nasally and patronizing tone coming from my "fearless" leader Barry. Barry was slim in build and tall. He was in his early thirties, insisted on wearing his hair in some kind of weird side sweep you'd see on a man twenty years older than him and his face caused a deep anger every time I was forced to look at it. It had a constant smug look slapped on its pale skin that made me want to punch him because it was so annoying, and his thin lips and eyes looked reptilian. He had a wife and kids, he used to love playing the family man and was perceived as quite a nice guy in a time before he got his leader promotion.

A few months after securing his new position he turned into a complete arsehole, treating people horribly, and began changing a lot in his personal life, including neglecting the family he used to enjoy rubbing in people's faces, as if being a dad gave him bragging rights. He was also a snitch, he was lazy, blunt and rude with everyone beneath his position and had very little communication skill. Barry rated himself very highly. Getting that leader's uniform was definitely the best day of his life; he truly thought he'd made something of himself and when he wore it, he thought he was a god among men.

"Few things to brief out, firstly when you go for your

break or lunch or whatever, you're no longer allowed to stand at the end of your line a minute before your break waiting for the clock to change, you are to continue working up until 12:30 or 10:00 and then you can turn your production light off and head to your break. From this point on if you are seen at the end of your line at 12:29 or 9:59 waiting for your lunch to start you will be taken into the office to discuss the matter. Secondly, as of next Monday, the way you will fill out your holiday requests will change. You will no longer be able to fill out your forms while you're on the line in work time. It's all being updated, and all requests will be done on the computer which is in the office. This will only be allowed to be done in your own time, either break times or at the start or the end of your shift. Anyone caught using the computer during work hours will be sent straight to the manager's office!"

"Hang on a minute," Mandy, one of the older operators said, interrupting him before he moved on. "Why are we having to do this on a computer now? What was wrong with the old forms? It took a minute to fill out while we were working and hand back to you."

"I don't know," was the instant reply, "that's just how they want it done from now on."

Mandy continued. "So how are we going to know how to fill out these new forms? I know myself and a few others struggle with using computers. That's why we work in a warehouse. If I could use a computer, I certainly wouldn't be working on a shop floor."

"Don't worry, all training will be provided, so when you go to use it for the first time come and grab either myself or another one of the leadership team and we will be happy to take you through it."

29

"In our own time?"

"In your own time," he repeated back with half a grin on his face. He was actually enjoying the frustration growing amongst his own staff.

Mandy continued. "So, you're going to train us to use the computer to create a holiday request in our own break time? So, what happens if we overrun on our break?"

Without even thinking or hesitating he replied, "Well, you either do it in your lunch break or if you overrun on your morning break, you can just make the time back at the end of your shift."

I scanned the group to look for the expressions on each one of their faces, and on most faces, it was just disgust but with no shock. This attitude towards us had been going on so long it just felt like another blow that caused no immediate pain, only us feeling that little bit more numb, and unappreciated.

Paul, another older member of the group, asked, "So, how do we know if the holiday has been approved if we have no further access to the computer after our break?"

"What do you mean?"

"You're saying that we have to go into the office in our own time and fill out the forms. How do we know if they've been accepted or not? When we filled out the old forms, we'd hand them to you and you would check on your computer to see if we could have it, then you would sign the form in front of us either accepting or declining the holiday, so how do we check it now? How will we know if the holiday has been accepted or not?"

"Once you've filled out the form online, come and see me and I'll be able to tell you whether it's been accepted or not!"

"So we still have to come to you anyway?"

"Yes!"

"So what's the point in filling it out on the computer if we then have to come and see you like we've always done?"

"Because they wanted a more efficient way of filling out and storing the holiday requests onto the system."

"But it's not more efficient, is it? You normally accept the request or decline it right then and there, now you're telling us we have to fill it out in one room and then come out into the warehouse, then try to find you, then get you to check the system for you to tell us if we have our holiday or not. It's going to take twice as long as it did before and if we're seen by the supervisors wandering around trying to find you, we're going to get in trouble."

"Look, I've just been told to brief this out. If you have any problems, you are more than welcome to go to Jimmy's or Rochelle's office and explain your concerns to them, anything else?"

"Yeah," Paul piping up once more, "I was speaking to one of our colleagues up in the stores last week and he told me this was only being rolled out in production, so not only did they know before any of us but he also said that it wasn't happening anywhere else, we're the only ones using this new holiday system, every other department is sticking with the old way! So what happened to being one company and everyone being treated the same way? Why are we being treated differently from everybody else in the company?"

"I don't know, Paul, I've been asked to brief this out and told if there are any problems you can go individually up to management and raise your concerns with them, right, anything else?"

There was no response to his question. As I looked around the group once more it was obvious there was still plenty to be said on the matter, but everyone knew it was pointless trying to say anything further. Barry was merely a messenger, a deflector of frustration and anger with no real authority or care to act on the responses of those it concerned. He was a verbal wall to bounce all the team's protestations off so the managers didn't have to deal with the consequences of their own ruthless decisions.

"Right, thirdly!" he shouted out, continuing his brief. "There's been a few changes to how you're allowed to get a coffee from the canteen. As of Monday, you will no longer be able to get a coffee in any more than groups of two! I'm sick of going into the canteen and seeing groups of three, four, sometimes five at the machines, we're losing too much build time on the lines and it's going to stop. If I find any groups in there of more than two hanging around the machines you will be sent to the manager's office! And also, as of Monday, you will no longer be able to enter the canteen for a drink between 8:00 and 8:30. If you want a drink between those times, you have to get it before the start of your shift or you'll have to wait until after half eight, anyone got anything to say about that?"

"Yeah, I have, Barry." I rarely said anything in the meetings. I really hated public speaking, I always tried to keep my head down but for me, this was a step too far. I was sick of him; I was sick of all of them. All they wanted to do was remove every little perk or privilege they could think of from us, and what pissed me off even more is every time they did it, they seemed to get some sort of kick out of it.

"I'm pretty sure you're not allowed to deny someone

access to water at any time."

"Excuse me?" he replied slightly taken aback that I was speaking and calling him out over the legalities of it.

"I'm fairly certain that as workers we are entitled to a supply of fresh drinking water, any time we feel the need to as it's important to keep hydrated. In fact, I'm pretty sure it's a human right, you can't deny us water at any time, and by restricting our access to the canteen you are in effect stopping us from getting water when we need to. Who authorised this?" I asked, emotion clearly coming through in my tone of voice. I never knew what our rights were, I've got to be honest, I knew next to nothing about employees' rights or employment laws; the only thing I knew is that he didn't either and it was obvious that this drink thing was his little idea. He had to read out all his managers' changes in the morning and thought if he rolled out a couple of his own in the process, he might get a biscuit and his tummy tickled by our department manager Rochelle when she found out, which is why I asked who authorised it because I knew no one had. Barry was a snake of a man, but I knew he certainly wouldn't drop his line manager in the shit for one of his stupid underthought ideas. He cared too much about how he was perceived by his superiors, he actually looked slightly panicked by my statement, he'd shot his mouth off without thinking it through and he was way too proud to fully retreat from it and admit he was wrong, so he stopped for a second to think under the instant building pressure to deliver a solution to his own stupid and pathetic problem.

"Right okay, if that's the case, you will only be allowed into the canteen between 8:00 and 8:30 for water only, no coffee." He looked down at the floor as soon as he said it, that smug grin stretching slightly wider than before. He was genuinely proud of himself and was taking a moment to enjoy the success of crawling out of that hole he dug himself into. Well done, Barry, don't forget to mention that little victory to Rochelle in your next appraisal, you're so the man!

"Anything else?" Of course, there was something else, but again it was pointless speaking to him about it. When there was no response from anyone, he began to read out the list of names and where they'd be working that day. When Barry had finished everyone began to disband. "Hold up," he said talking to me without even bothering to address me by my name, instead waving me back over to his presence, "I need to have a chat with you."

"Yeah sure, what's up?"

"You were late this morning."

"I think you'll find I wasn't, Barry, I clocked in at five to."

"No, it doesn't matter what time you clock in. You are supposed to be at the morning brief before eight for the meeting to begin at exactly eight o'clock."

"I was on time for the brief."

"You were still walking towards the team when I began the meeting."

"Are you being serious? I was literally three steps away when you started talking."

"I'm deadly serious, technically you were late."

"I haven't been late in months, Barry, I clocked in before the start time this morning and I was at the meeting at the stroke of eight. I wasn't late. I have not only hit my targets on line, I have exceeded them every day for well over a year, which is more than any other operator can boast in this place. I go above and beyond, taking on last minute orders and staying late on occasion to see them through, which I don't have to do, but I know it helps you and the team out, and I train anyone who walks through these doors and get them up to a decent standard in very good time and you want to confront me over three seconds at most!?"

I was fuming. Three seconds! I was in clear bloody view; I was practically in the group when the clock turned.

Without hesitation he said, "I appreciate what you do but…"

"Clearly because you're pulling me up over something like this!" I felt the blood rush to my face almost instantly. My heart was pounding heavily in my chest. I got so angry so quickly, I was really struggling to contain it.

"Eight o'clock is your start time. If you don't want me to have these little chats with you, then make sure you're at the meeting before eight o'clock ready to start your shift and if you have a problem with what I've just said, you are more than welcome to take it to management or even HR." He looked right at me when he said it and made no effort to stop looking so cocky and smarmy.

I just walked straight to the line I was training on ignoring anything else he had to say; he'd been an unbelievably petty little man. I get it I was late, technically, even though I clocked in on time. I was banged to rights in the sense that I knew what their policy was and I breached it, but come on, it was by the narrowest of margins. I could understand the need for Barry to address it if I had a poor attitude or I was consistently late but I wasn't and I was the hardest worker they had by a country mile, always going above and beyond; he was so pathetic he just had to make something of three seconds on one occasion; I was so angry after that.

He did it because I answered him back in the meeting. Because I questioned his authority, and he didn't know how to respond to it appropriately and with maturity. He lacked the skills to actually engage with people. To compensate for this, he did three things in the workplace effectively, oppress, be a yes man and suck up to his boss like it was going out of fashion. A man of reason or logic would understand we're all human, we all make mistakes from time to time, but that way of thinking never entered his mind. His mind was built purely to do things he thought would impress his manager and perform acts he thought would get him noticed in the right way. He was always quick to dish out rules, warnings and punishments but not once in the eighteen months of being there did I ever receive a "thank you", a "well done" or "good job" or a single piece of gratitude for all the hard work! He was everything a supervisor shouldn't be, including a drug-taking little groomer, an adulterer and a hypocrite; we will cover all that later in the book.

I spent the rest of that morning trying to calm myself down and by the afternoon, I felt really low. I had lost faith in the system I was contributing to, hope of a better or more peaceful life looked beyond my reach and was starting to unravel as the lie I'd been feeding myself for years.

These scenarios, these kinds of stories happen every day across the country in various different companies and sectors. The bootlicking, the ruthlessness and trampling to progress and every time I've spoken out about this to friends and family about how it pisses me off, every time I get the same response, "That's life, mate", "People are selfish, what can you do?" My brother once told me, "The world is all about self-gain, it's not how it should be but that's just how it is and there's nothing you can do to change it." What drives me crazy about all their responses is why? Why is it deemed normal or acceptable? What about social standards, morals and principles? We spend years as parents and elders encouraging our children to grow up with honesty and integrity, to be respectable, respectful people and live, in hope, that one day they will develop empathy and understanding along the way and become upstanding citizens and fine human beings that can deal with all the curveballs life can throw at them, yet as soon as they hit working life and the barriers of parenthood are lifted on their journey these young people are thrust into selfish environments. They are suddenly pushed to possess a self-serving lifestyle and encouraged to climb up the work ladder at every opportunity even at the cost of their principles as well as treading on friends and colleagues to get there.

There was no point going to the supervisors about what was said in the morning brief. They were just the same as Barry; the only difference is that they wore a white shirt instead of a red polo with the company logo stitched on. They were just as useless and thought they were the bee's knees too! They spent every day justifying their job's existence with shitty, horrible ideas that affected their staff in negative ways rather than actually working with others, which is what they were paid to do. They cared more about their new haircut and if it presented the right image more than they ever did about their employees' welfare. All the supervisors were a closed-off group. They only ever spoke to you if they benefited in some way from it or felt it would be a potential stain on their work reputation if they didn't speak to you or they were punishing you formally in some way. They were supposed to be our points of contact at work, they were supposed to engage with us and build a rapport with us, but the reality was that I'd never said more than two sentences to any of the supervisors in the entire time I'd been there and that was only when I had been absent from work and had to go through a return interview. They were just never around, and they weren't interested in anyone but themselves. I know for a fact they were supposed to engage with their staff regularly as I'd spoken to a director of the company who told me that's what they should be doing as part of their duties, but they weren't, and they never seemed to be challenged on it either, which told me they were pulling the wool over their employer's eyes pretending to be engaging with us when they weren't.

So they neglected all their responsibilities, they didn't engage with staff unless there's a bigwig from upstairs looking on them or they felt their job was under threat. They lied to their superiors except Rochelle (their line manager), they didn't praise, motivate, train or encourage, they punished, dismissed and humiliated people in their care. They also had good ideas for improvements to the business from operators and posed them as their own and still, despite all of this, they walked around with such arrogance, classing themselves as successful businessmen because they were no longer on the bottom looking up and they wore a white company shirt. Successful? Really, guys? Tell me how you are successful exactly? How? What makes you suddenly better than the rest of us? Because when all is said and done, you're not exactly in the boardroom making top financial decisions, are you? You've just been wrongly promoted up a notch from the bottom of a very long ladder in a tiny little warehouse in a small rural town in Nowheresville. You lied in your interview to get the job, you lie to your bosses every day to keep the job and eventually, when your lies catch up with you, all the talk of caring passionately about the company and its values will go out the window and you'll jump ship within five years to the next poor sucker who takes you in because you have the word supervisor or leader uploaded on your CV!

At first, I used to always blame companies and

corporations for the treatment of low-level employees, thinking that the decision makers sat so high up in the chain they couldn't see what was going on beneath them and they wouldn't care anyway. I blamed them like so many others because it was easy to do so, because it suited my argument of us and them! The rich vs poor, the unskilled average working man versus the giants of upper class and management, owners and directors, but I don't blame them any more. They front and lead the business and make sure of its success. It's supposed to be us employed beneath them that work out how we treat each other within the structure. So I'm pointing the finger at us in the lower levels, I blame us for how we are being treated by the corporations and I blame us for what we have allowed ourselves to become, and that's rats in a sinking ship. There is no real communication between the two worlds any more, and it's our fault. Our perks are taken away, our rights stretched, and we have lost respect for ourselves and others because we break every moral and let go of every principle to chase a concept that simply doesn't exist, success. So many of us now are going through life concerned about what we are and how we're defined by our roles and statuses, the job we do and what it says about us rather than who we could be, what we can do and how we treat others. It appears more now than ever that we have a growing middle management in our society filled with self-obsessed, lying chancers who have climbed from the bottom who are more concerned about the private parking space they have been given and the tie they wear that day rather than the people they are supposed to represent and be responsible for, exceptions always existing contrary to this, of course.

# Chapter Two
# Starting out

At the age of twenty-seven, I found myself with quite an extensive job history. I'd worked in many different positions over various sectors from data entry at a bank to a supervisor/delivery driver at an agricultural company that delivered spraying chemicals to farms.

It was always my intention to go straight to college when I left school. I wanted to study sports science and sociology. I was sports mad as a teenager and although I wasn't a hundred percent sure what I wanted to do, I knew it had to be around activities, fitness and being outdoors. Plus, the idea of avoiding full-time working life for another couple of years while I went to college really appealed to me. Just before I turned sixteen my next to useless stepfather decided to up and split, demanding a divorce while leaving my mother with absolutely nothing, not even enough to pay his half of the bills that were piling up on the kitchen side. So I put my ideas of college, sports and avoiding work to one side and decided it was probably best I found myself a job and helped with the rent. My mum never asked me to do it, she would never dream of putting me in such a position. If I had told her of my desires to go to college, I know she would have done everything in her power to make sure it happened, so I couldn't tell her. The decision was about the sort of person I wanted to be and a big part of that was being able to get up every morning, look in the mirror and be proud of the person staring back at me and there's no way I'd even be able to glance up at myself if I knew I made my mother struggle a few years more while I dossed through college; I just couldn't be that guy. Life throws you a curveball sometimes, it never goes the way you intend. I was entering the real world, and these were the choices that came with it.

I finished the last of my school exams in the May of 2003. My sixteenth birthday came in the July of that year. The day I hit sixteen I started the job hunt immediately. I didn't like sitting still for too long. I applied to every large or major business in the town, insurance companies, restaurants, supermarkets, fast food chains — you name it, I probably had their application form in my house at some point on my dining room table. I managed to get to the interview stage with a few of the applications but I got pretty much the same response from all: "Dear Mr Allan, thank you very much for your interest in our job opening. Unfortunately, you have been unsuccessful on this occasion... blah blah blah." At the time I began to wonder if my interview skills really sucked; maybe I looked too eager to stack shelves and came across as a little crazy but I just wanted to start earning money. After about four weeks of applying and interviewing I'd had no luck at all until my older cousin came over to the house one afternoon. No time to knock, he just let himself in the front door as the lock was always on the catch and walked straight up the stairs to my room where I was sprawled across my bed in my underpants playing computer games.

"Hey cuz, you, all right?"

"All right, mate, how's it going? Fancy a game?"

"Ah I can't, mate, thank you. I haven't really got the time. I just popped over to tell you I had some good news!"

"Oh yeah, what's that then?" I asked as I turned back around to the television and took my game off pause.

"I've got you a job, mate."

I paused the game again. "Seriously?"

"Yeah, seriously, you've got an interview on Monday. I'm coming over at twelve to pick you up and take you to meet your manager."

"I don't know what to say. Thank you so much, what's the job?"

"You're going to be a waiter at a roadside café. Now I know it's not glamorous or mega money but it's a job and you also get tips as well, which helps."

"How do you know the job is mine if I have to go for the interview?"

"The interview is standard procedure but they are so desperate for staff they'll take you on, plus I've recommended you and I know the manager. I said you were a top guy and would work hard, so don't let me down."

"I won't, mate, thanks again. I really appreciate this."

"No need to thank me, just make sure you graft, now I've gotta dash. I'll pick you up on Monday. Make sure you're ready to go, right, I'll see you later."

I was so excited, my first job. I would be on the minimum wage which was four pound fifty an hour at that time, but I didn't care. I'd taken weeks of solid rejection prior to my cousin's visit. I was beginning to feel as though I was completely unemployable. I was just so grateful to have a job at the end of it.

After working out a sizable rent for my mum I was

picturing in my head how I was going to spend the rest of my first set of wages. At that age you think roughly a thousand pound a month would mean an endless supply of "whatever I want" clothes, shoes, computer games, videos and junk, but then reality slaps you right in the face and you learn very quickly life just doesn't work like that, money disappears very quickly on the have to's: rent, food, shopping, driving lessons, bills, dentist and parking tickets. By the time I received my second pay slip those pictures of lavish spending in my head were quickly replaced by budget and balance.

Ten o'clock the following Monday morning and my adrenaline was in full swing. I was pacing up and down the house frantically. I had my neatly ironed old school trousers on, ever so slightly frayed at the bottom, but they were the only pair I owned. My shoes had been polished and layered so much a sergeant major would have been proud and I was moving through the house pacing up and down the living room and hallway with no shirt on. Despite the fact I'd only showered half an hour before I was sweating profusely because of all the nerves, and deodorant just wasn't cutting it, so I had left it off until the very last minute to allow my body to air as much as possible; it was to avoid pockets of sweat appearing from my armpits on my very first day in my first job. I'd had about three coffees that morning, which certainly didn't help with the sweating and pacing but making and drinking it had helped pass the time and I'd also had no breakfast. There was no way I could have eaten anything; I felt so sick and sweaty. I wanted twelve o'clock to hurry up and come so that I could get it over with. I was constantly looking at the living room clock as I passed it, begging the hands to move that little bit faster, but they didn't. In fact, I checked it so often it looked as if they were weren't moving at all. Eventually I got tired of pacing up and down the house and peering out the kitchen window every minute to see if my cousin was going to turn up and collect me two hours early so I perched myself at the base of the staircase and tried to compose myself. I wished my brother or mum would have been at home that morning to calm me down a bit and tell me everything was going to be fine, tell me there was no need to be nervous or at the very least distract me from my anxieties. There was normally always someone in the house when I didn't want them to be, but the one morning I wanted them to actually be there, they were both out. When I finally calmed down a little, my sweating subsided, and my thinking became a bit more rational. I began recalling all the things my grandfather told me about work and becoming an adult.

My grandfather was a remarkable man and the most humble person, I've ever known. He was actually my mother's stepfather and although he wasn't "blood" related, he'd been married to my nan well over twenty years before I was born and treated every one of us (grandchildren in the family) as his own and I loved him just as much as my other grandparents; he was there from the moment we were all born and we knew nothing different. He'd been a labourer all his life; hard work was his only skill set, and graft was the only language he spoke in a job. He worked on roads, building sites and major projects for construction companies pretty much all his adult life. He worked twelve-hour days every day no matter the weather, conditions or pay and he never ever moaned about his lot in life. Some of my earliest memories of him when I was a child would be my grandfather cycling home in his work gear after a long day while my brother and I were playing in his garden. He'd go in, clean up and sit down to the meal my nan had prepared for him and eat it in front of the TV while he soaked his broken feet in salt water to help clean out the bloody blisters he'd developed from that day. He would stay up for a couple of hours, and when his head began dipping in the chair, he'd go off to bed to ready himself for another day's grind!

The times I would spend with my grandad were quality times. He'd often take the grandchildren on long walks into the countryside on a Sunday afternoon and do what we liked to call scavenger hunts. We would take in the beautiful views around us and collect any odd bits and bobs we found on our way. Nuts, bolts, screws, bits of wood, metal, all things that had been dumped by fly tippers or parts dropped by mistake. He would collect them up, store in his little brick shed attached to the side of his house and try to make use of what he'd found. Somebody dumped a broken shed or dining table? Not a problem, grandad salvaged the wood and turned them into a dog kennel. Somebody tipped a broken wardrobe? Grandad got some shelves from the heap they left. He could pretty much turn his hand to anything, and it would always be from scraps here and there he would find on his travels. During these walks he would always talk to me about life, dropping little nuggets of wisdom in my ear or discussing fascinating things he'd seen on a documentary. His thirst for knowledge and his excitement in sharing what he'd discovered blew me away. I always looked forward to our Sunday chats. As I got to my teens, he began to talk to me more and more about working and becoming a man. He would never lecture me about it, though; that wasn't his way. He would often tell me stories about his working life and explain the lessons to be learned from it. I think it was his way of trying to prepare me as much as possible for the world I'd face one day. He'd say things in a simple and broken-down way leaving no room for interpretation like, "When you're asked to do something by your boss and there's a group of you, it doesn't matter what they're doing, they could be standing around chatting or slacking off, you do what's asked of you, keep your head down and get on with what you're supposed to be doing. If he's asked all of you to be getting on with something and they're all still standing around, don't be pressured to stand with them; they don't pay your wages."

"Always do what is asked of you and nothing more! Otherwise, people will see you as someone they can take advantage of."

"Never suck up to the boss. You'll get his attention but you'll never get his respect. If you want his respect, then do what you are supposed to be doing and nothing else."

"Never tell on anyone, you'll make the wrong name for yourself, concentrate on what you do. Their business is their own."

"If someone works hard for their money, they deserve your respect. It doesn't matter if they clean windows, toilets or if they are a manager. If they're making an honest living and they're working hard, then they deserve your respect! Always."

As I sat there on those stairs with all the years of conversations and pieces of advice flowing through my mind, I realised I was more prepared for a job than I first thought and it was all thanks to my wise labouring grandfather. Work experience provided by my school a couple of years before prepared me for what a working environment would be like, what it looked like, getting the chance to observe the day-to-day running of a business or company, which was valuable experience, don't get me wrong, but it was Grandad who taught me how to deal with people, to be courteous and polite. He explained why it was important to work hard and always reminded me to pay respect to those who had earned it. He taught me that work was never about climbing a ladder or making a name for yourself, it was about maintaining decency and staying true to your morals and principles despite any temptations and that success could be achieved when the time was right rather than something to be chased and hunted down just to gain a little more money and status.

Five past twelve and my cousin pulled up in the drive outside the house. He was late, so I was late, and I could feel the sweat once more beginning to build up around my body. I had one more spray of deodorant, put my shirt and tie on, one last check in the mirror to make sure there wasn't a hair out of place or toothpaste around my mouth and went out to the car.

"Sorry I'm late, cuz, come on jump in, let's go, don't worry, I'll explain why you're late."

"Shit, I was nervous enough already."

"Relax, relax, I know the guy, you're going to be fine, don't overthink it."

We entered onto the A road just outside town and travelled along for about a mile before we took a turn off into a services and rest area. As we pulled up there was a large petrol station over on the far right of the court and in front of me was a small single floored and dated building that looked as though it should have been pulled down and started again because it was hideous. It wasn't in any sort of disrepair but my first impression of it was that it didn't look very welcoming at all. It was cold and business-like in appearance, as though it had been converted from a small office unit into a restaurant. If I had pulled up to this establishment looking for something to eat and saw the building for the first time, I wouldn't even be tempted to stop there and eat. Dark orange brickwork with dark brown trim and window frames, black tiles and no outside lighting, advertising so minimal you wouldn't even be certain it was a restaurant/café unless your eyes caught the large sun-faded sign screwed to the brickwork at the side of the building as you drove in. There was only one other small sign with the company's logo above the door, again faded. I'd like to find the person responsible for this advertising strategy so that I could avoid them if I ever went into business.

We went in through the main entrance, my cousin leading the way, and instantly I was greeted by the stale smell of greasy fry ups mixed with cheap cleaning products.

"Wait here a sec, I'll go and find Chris," my cousin said as he turned left and headed off into the kitchen area leaving me to take in my surroundings. The interior somehow managed to appear worse than the outside. The tables were all dark brown with cheap, basic wooden chairs to accompany them, no place mats or cutlery laid out, just a holder containing a few worn-out paper menus on each tabletop. The carpets appeared to be the original fitting, which meant at least thirty years old, burgundy in colour with little floral patterns running throughout. On closer inspection there were years of staining and discolouration on it. The seating was divided into two areas. The main area being a raised floor by a single step on my right which seated roughly a hundred people over various sized tables; the edge of this area was cordoned off with a black metal railing topped with a dark wood finish that ran the whole way around except for two entry points. The rest of the tables were positioned on the other side of this railing at ground level seating roughly another thirty. I looked over to the left of me at the only area that looked like it had received any sort of attention within the last twenty years, the kitchen and prep area. The floor and the walls looked bright, modern and clean. Every counter and shelf were stainless steel and the kitchen could be seen fairly openly from the restaurant, so customers could see their food being prepared in front of them. I was quite impressed with it; it looked as though they were willing to invest a little money at least in the kitchen area to keep up with modern day hygiene standards. It was just a shame they left the restaurant/seating area to rely on a fading company reputation. Just as I finished absorbing the dated diner a short and plump figure appeared to the left of me, gliding from around the corner like an overweight dancer sliding into my view from the kitchen area. "Hi, I'm Chris, nice to meet you, how are you doing?"

Chris was the restaurant and site manager. He stood about five foot ten, balding black hair and what was left of it looked fluffy and frail. He had a strong and distinct Welsh accent. He had slightly goofy teeth surrounded by an unkempt stubble. He was wearing grey suit trousers with a matching waistcoat that was struggling to fit him around the belly. The base of the waistcoat was all crumpled where he had to keep pulling it back down, most likely riding up over his gut when he sat down. He was either too lazy to put the order in for a new one or he was in a sense of denial he needed to go up a few sizes. Chris was supposed to be the top dog in the place and looked as though he had just stepped out of a council estate wedding reception for a fag. To finish off the look he accompanied his manager's uniform with big clumpy shoes, old but not worn, which combined with his heavy size told me he didn't do much

49

of the running about and assisting his staff.

"I'm well, thank you, Chris, nice to meet you."

"Would you like to follow me into the office?"

I made my way through to the tiny cupboard-like room he called his office. Inside was a second-hand desk with the most dated and basic of computers sat on top. There was an office chair next to the desk, black leather and completely worn on the seat; one of the five plastic base wheels was missing. I sat down in the visitor's chair, a stainless-steel product with several holes throughout the thick lime green fabric that covered the frame, exposing the dark orange sponge that provided its comfort; it looked more like an old school builder's portacabin than a restaurant manager's hub.

The walls were supposed to be magnolia in colour, but the grease had made its way through the doorway over the years and had stained them gradually and badly. It looked as though someone had thrown around a box of used tea bags in the room and no one could be bothered to clean up the mess.

There was one small window on the far wall looking out over the petrol station like a pathetic box-ticking attempt of letting in light and life into this crummy little space to make it an office... and not a cupboard.

"So I just need you to fill out these application forms and then we can get you started on your computer training."

"Oh, right, I see, sorry, I didn't realise I'd got the job. I thought I was here for an interview."

"Well, it's not guaranteed at this point. You will be on a probation period for the first three months, see how you get on and if you're up to the job we will take you on, on a permanent contract."

"Fair enough, okay, great!"

"Right, once we've finished your application form, we'll crack on with your computer-based training and when that's done, I'll get you some uniform and then you can start work."

"Today?"

"Yes today, is that a problem?"

"No, not a problem. I just didn't realise I would be actually starting today. I thought I was just coming in for an interview, then I would leave and hear back if I was successful or not at a later date."

"Well, do you want the job or not?" he asked dismissively. I felt his question was rather rude and rather abrupt for a man I'd only known for two minutes, not exactly welcoming or inspiring. I realised I must have appeared uninterested with my responses, but it was more a case of being unprepared and off guard. My cousin hadn't told me there would be a chance I was starting that day, he told me it was just an interview. It was clear some wires had been crossed and it had created an awkward first encounter. The fact that I was eager to start my first job and also the fact that he looked from his tired, shabby appearance as though he'd spent the night before sleeping in his office, I decided to give Chris the benefit of the doubt. I swallowed my pride regarding the embarrassment and accepted his proposal.

I spent about three and a half hours solid going through all the computer-based training. Basic food hygiene, company policies, health and safety, duties, customer service, the levels of conduct and professionalism required from their employees, and let me tell you, they expected a lot for their four pound fifty an hour. When all of that was completed, I was sent into the staff room at the back of the kitchen, the far corner of the building into another little soulless cupboard-like space which contained no effort or personality in its décor.

"Okay," Chris said, "here's your uniform. We found some in your size and we'll order some more for you now and they should be here by the end of the week. Until then make do with these."

He left the room and I opened the black refuse sack to examine the second-hand, former employee's uniform I had to wear, great... It looked like the bloody restaurant carpet! Well, the shirt did, and it had a few faint stains on it to complete the look. The trousers were dark blue and didn't exactly match my smartly polished school shoes, so when I put it all together it looked as though I'd got dressed in the dark out of a really crap lost and found! After I was changed, I had a quick tour of the kitchens. Then I had soft drinks training; after that I was put straight out onto the restaurant floor to take orders and wait tables for the remainder of my shift. Chris watched me seat a couple of customers, then returned to his office, and that was about the entire extent of his managerial /training input.

Seven months later

And I'm the king of the kitchens, lord of the till and the master of waiting tables. I had become the fastest and hardest worker in the place. By this time, I knew the whole restaurant like the back of my hand. There was nobody that could match my speed and efficiency and I'm not being arrogant or big headed at all. I was constantly told by my colleagues and supervisors about my high standard. I worked so hard because I really loved my job and they all liked me being part of their team and that pride and that feeling of belonging raised my game. I was proud to be a young working man and I didn't care that it was waiting tables either. I enjoyed the fast pace of it all while sometimes under a little pressure to maintain a good service. There were occasions we couldn't always satisfy every customer that came through our doors, but we always tried our best. I was part of a very good group. Some of the staff were there full-time, and had been in the business a few years, some were part time, students looking to save some much-needed money or full-time parents holding an evening role to earn some extra cash. All different walks of life but everyone seemed to enjoy their work and being part of the team. By this time, I'd been trained on all courses available to me. I was also competent in every area of the restaurant, including the kitchen. There were also little perks the job had to offer too. A share of the tips, unlimited soft drinks all shift and a free meal every lunchtime; my shirts were becoming stretched to breaking point around the gut dining out on the greasy menu and knocking back sugary drinks every day.

There were only two things about the job I didn't like and the first one was Chris the manager, and that's because, in all honesty, he turned out to be a bit of a pig. I didn't have some sort of deep-seated, underlying problem with authority. I got along very well with all the shift supervisors; it was just him I didn't like. I'll give you an example of what he was like.

Every bank holiday weekend the restaurant was absolutely packed to the brim from the moment the doors opened to the moment it closed at ten pm. People would pour into the place from their family days out, looking to begin their day with a hot breakfast or end their adventures with a nice meal before they returned home. Every member of staff would dread this weekend, why? Because it was like being assigned to a slowly sinking ship, that's why. No matter how hard or fast you worked you were going to gradually fall behind on the orders, the cleaning, the washing up, everything, because the line of customers was never ending. It was guaranteed to be a long, hard day with several hours of cleaning to do after the restaurant closed in order to get it ready for the next day, sometimes staying as late as two the next morning cleaning and prepping everything; it really was full on. The way the company compensated for this explosion of business would be to reward the staff working with a double hourly rate, a great and fair incentive from the business, but no one at our restaurant wanted to work it because of Chris. The only time of the year you would ever see him do any overtime would be a bank holiday in which he put himself on a double shift at double pay at manager's rates and everyone knew it would be a wasted allocation of staffing because he didn't lift a finger, wash a single cup or clear a single plate away, putting even more pressure on the rest of the staff that were rushing around all weekend. The rule was if you signed up to work the bank holiday, manager or not, you had to roll up your sleeves. He knew this, ignored it and took the money. You wouldn't see him for the entire day except for once right in the middle of the afternoon rush. The kitchen already with too many orders they almost couldn't cope was when he decided he would waddle out of his office and add a large family-sized pizza with extra toppings for himself to the orders list and it had to be delivered to his office by one of his overworked staff members. His attitude stunk and I found it extremely difficult to find something likeable about him. He never helped out with the running of the restaurant even if we were short staffed. I was told by long-serving team members who worked under other managers in the same chain that he was supposed to be the front of house, to be the face of the business, but the customers never saw him. He rarely ever completed a full shift either, always leaving early and arriving late but taking full pay nonetheless, and he never helped in the clean downs. The only time he would ever venture out of his cupboard was if an area manager was visiting. Then he'd quickly straighten his clothes, leap out of his chair and pucker up! They would often come in and be in the role of the customer to see and experience things from their perspective, they'd come in for tea or something to eat and that's when he'd throw on his cape and parade around the place like super waiter, directing other members of staff and instructing them to do things they were already doing to appear involved and in control. I was amazed at times by his ability to multitask, whizzing around remembering his duties whilst being able to sniff the butts of his superiors at the same time; it really was quite a skill and it was cringey watching him. Once they'd leave, he'd go straight back in the office and close the door behind him to go and play games on his laptop or phone pretending to be deeply involved in office work but he had been caught too many times doing it for it to be conceivable. The phrase "lead by example" had completely bypassed this man. He was constantly rude and paid no attention to the welfare of his staff except for the married, female supervisor he was shagging. Unfortunately, that wasn't just a rumour I'd heard. I had the eye-burning experience of witnessing their entangled sweaty bodies going at it first-hand one night when walking home, spotting his work vehicle in a poorly lit car park steaming up with what I can only describe as two elephants wrestling in the back seat. That aside, how can you expect to manage a team effectively in such a way? Literally pretend to do your job in front of the right people and then when their backs are turned possess the cheek to dump on those directly around you. Two-faced, spineless behaviour giving absolutely no respect or consideration to those in his employment.

You can choose to be any sort of person you wish to in this world. That is your right, but you can never neglect your duties at the expense of putting your workload onto others and then regard yourself as a decent person. He tried, but no one ever bought it, and he pushed his whole team away as a result.

The second thing that bothered me about the job was my pay. I was still on four pound fifty an hour, which to begin with was fair enough. I'd accepted the job at that rate, but I was also promised by the manager the more courses I did the more my pay would reflect that. As I've already mentioned I completed every course available to me and I was fully trained in every area of the restaurant and there was still no increase. I was then promised a pay rise once I'd become a cook in the restaurant. Well, by this time I was one of two main cooks and between our shifts we covered all the opening hours and guess what? My pay rise still didn't come or was even mentioned. It really annoyed me because the other cook and I did exactly the same job and he was on six pound an hour. Well, I say exactly the same job — in truth he was a total slob. I always took great pride in the cleanliness of my kitchen, and he couldn't really give a crap. Every day we'd have to do a handover and I always made sure I'd leave the kitchen as I found it, clean, all hygiene standards met, food all temp checked and recorded and all prep completed; there wouldn't be a thing out of place. When it was my turn to take over from him it was like walking into a war zone, it was as though someone had set off a grenade on the griddle and did a runner! There would be dirty plates everywhere, sauce on every counter, broken eggs splattered on the floor, there would be bits of food on every shelf and surface imaginable like he'd had some sort of cooking meltdown. The prep would never be done, food checks never completed and sometimes I would come across something disgusting as a result of his laziness like raw gammon sitting in a fresh salad tray that he'd just shoved back into the walk-in fridge assuming someone would still use it to garnish meals. James (the other cook) had no excuse for this behaviour. He just couldn't be bothered. His only interest was his rock band, and work was merely a stopgap until they made it. He followed his boss's example of sucking up to his superiors and dumping his workload onto me. I was basically carrying this dirty, long-haired clown and he was being paid a lot more than me to do it and it wasn't fair.

I'd kept up my end of the deal, but Chris wasn't being true to his word and that simply wasn't good enough. I'd discussed the whole thing at length with my grandfather and he agreed I needed to address the issue once more with my manager. "Your word is your bond, and it's all a man really has," he'd say to me.

Knock, knock, on his office door, finding a moment when the restaurant was quiet. There was a delay, probably while he paused his game.

"Come in."

"All right, Chris, I was wondering if I can have a quick chat with you about something."

"Course you can," he responded in the flattest way possible and not even bothering to make eye contact, "Close the door take a seat and tell me what's up."

"As you know, Chris, I've been one of the main cooks

here for a couple months now, I'm good at it, I always turn up on time, I always put in the hours and I'm flexible with it and I never complain."

"Yes."

"Well, I was wondering when the raise in pay will come in like we had discussed when I was put into the kitchen?"

Instantly uncomfortable with my question, he adjusted himself on his broken swivel seat to begin slowly facing away from me.

"You do a remarkable job in there, it's true, and you are certainly one of the best members of staff I have, but the budget here for the restaurant is quite tight, head office are already asking me to tighten it up a bit as they feel we're already spending too much, so I'm sorry, I just can't justify raising your hourly rate right now and pushing the budget further."

"Right."

"Okay, is there anything else I can help with?"

"No, that was it," clearly showing disappointment.

"Like I said, you're a great member of the team and if there was anything I could do, to get you your raise, I would do it but it's just not possible at this time."

"Okay, well, thanks for your time."

No, no! I can't believe I said no. I wish I could go back to that sixteen-year-old me and shake some bloody sense into him. Chris knew what we had agreed when I took the new role. He was also being dishonest. He had just sidestepped the issue and fed me a load of bull to get me to carry on doing what he wanted at the lowest cost possible and I was too spineless to challenge him on it. He took advantage of a shy teenager who was frightened of losing his first job if he overstepped the mark. I'd talked it through with my family previously and I had it in my head what I was going to say to him but when I was there in front of him in his office, I bottled it.

I left his office feeling a bit upset he hadn't kept his word and wasn't prepared to do anything. I felt embarrassed that I'd been taken for granted and angry at myself too, for not challenging any of it.

I told Dawn, my supervisor, what had happened.

And she too was upset by his response because she knew he had the authority to do something about it. He controlled the budget, but adding more cost would mean sticking his neck out and running the risk of looking bad at head office and that was too much for him; it was just easier to go against his word and let someone down who wouldn't challenge him.

I returned home from work later that night still upset and concluded his response simply wasn't good enough. I could no longer work for a person whose word meant nothing. He had told me I was one of his best, but I was also his lowest paid and that wouldn't be changing anytime in the near future. I needed to retain some self-worth and respect because I knew once I allowed that sort of thing to happen once, he could walk all over me whenever he needed to. So, I began to make some calls to family and friends to see if there were any vacancies at their places of work and after a couple of hours one of my school mates had pulled through. He managed to arrange an interview with a parcel company in the town three days later.

I got the time off work and went to the interview. It went well, and I was offered the job, which I accepted after I worked through my notice.

I was relieved once I knew I was leaving. I was the one feeling embarrassed by the situation that had been created and it should have been Chris. My manager should have carried some weight of shame, but he really couldn't have cared less until I returned to work after my interview to tell him I'd found another job. He looked genuinely surprised and gutted at the news. I know it wasn't because he was going to miss me as a person. He was gutted because in that moment he realised he was going to be worse off. He had me on four fifty an hour, because that was the lowest rate he could drop to, for someone my age, but what if none of the applicants for my job were sixteen? That meant he would have to employ to a wage probably nearer the amount I wanted to be raised to and would have to go all through the training again in the hope there was a half-decent employee at the end of it.

It was the wrong decision. I was a good employee who loved his job and would have stayed and continued to work hard had he fulfilled his promise, but he was just a bad manager. There may have been a time when he was a good employee himself. He must have shown something to reach that position in the beginning, but his trouble was he had become lazy and complacent, showing no desire to improve or develop his leadership. Instead, he sat back in that role and watched every attribute that got him there gradually be replaced with rudeness, disregard and a complete lack of respect for others, relying on the status of being a manager rather than taking his responsibilities seriously.

# Chapter Three
# Work experience

## Logistics and manual handling

After I left the roadside café, I went to work at the parcel company on an industrial estate on the other side of town in what they called their part-time evening shift. The job was only thirty hours a week but with the hourly rate at five pound and seventy-nine pence an hour and, compared to the old four pound fifty I had been on previously, there wasn't much difference in the wage packet after tax. Besides, there was always an extra couple of hours here and there I could pick up and bump up the weekly wage slip; the depot was always busy.

It was a huge contrast to the only working environment I'd known before. The people I'd worked with before were all clean, tidy, polite and customer-orientated people. I would now be working with the complete opposite. Mostly all lads around my own age. There were roughly twenty of them on the evening shift and they all looked as though they had accidentally wandered in from the roughest council estates in the area judging by their appearance. They all smoked heavily, they all mumbled and made no effort to speak properly and they all seemed to lack the possession of a fingernail brush at home or the knowledge on how to actually use one. All their hair was in a complete overgrown mess, tucked and stuffed in underneath their brand name beanie hats and all wore half uniforms where their clothes kept getting snagged, caught and ripped by the demanding and sometimes awkward nature of the job. The company couldn't seem to replace their uniforms quick enough or they didn't want to, so the lads started wearing their own jeans, hoodies and safety boots in.

The job was simple enough, but it was hard work. Twenty of us would clock in and start at four in the afternoon, around the time most people would think about winding down from their work days and we would have to move eighty tonnes of freight in those six hours from eighteen collection bays in the warehouse where over forty-seven-and-a-half tonne lorries would be shunted in at that time. We had to remove and sort all the freight from these vehicles and stack them in the appropriate eighteen vehicles on the opposite side of the warehouse to be shipped out to all the other depots around the country and there was a slight time pressure too. Some vehicles had to make their way up as far as Scotland from Hampshire by the following morning in order to make the next day deliveries. So that particular vehicle had to be filled, locked and out of the yard by eight o'clock each night and not a minute past. Like I said, it wasn't complicated at all, but it was hard, physical work and it wasn't made any easier by the standards of the place. You see, manual handling and health and safety must have somehow bypassed this nationwide and reputable company when they were being rolled out because we were given no training at all in how to lift things correctly and all we had were sack trucks. Which sounds like sufficient equipment when you picture a parcel company, delivering all the little packages and jiffy bags you're likely to receive on your doorsteps, but our customer base was businesses and we got the more industrial side of the freight market. 100kg, 200kg, 300kg carpets and up to fifteen feet long to go to the showrooms, kitchen fittings, building materials, metal lifts to repair and store motorcycles, industrial cleaning chemicals with God only knows what inside the drums and bottles. You name something awkward, dangerous or heavy that needed delivering in the country, chances are they probably came through one of our eighteen doors. It seemed like we were the only company that took all the awkward crap that no other delivery company wanted to touch. We were driven by a sales team that received a huge percentage of profit from the contracts they secured, so they would sling anything our way if it lined their pockets, and they didn't really care if we had the equipment to deal with it or not. We were the only local depot that didn't own a conveyor/sorting belt in its warehouse because it would have been counterproductive in dealing with the freight we took. Instead, we had ten-year-old bodge repaired sack trucks with bent frames and wobbly wheels, some repaired with nails instead of split pins to keep the wheels attached to the frame. We also had a set of out-of-date pump trucks and a prayer to move the freight and that was it. It was an awkward, tough and sometimes dangerous environment, but I loved it.

The scruffy guys with tough exteriors I met on my first day became my good friends after a while. Over time our friendships then spilled over beyond the boundaries of work, going out for meals and beers together on the weekends and we became a tight crew. I even grew a set of dirty fingernails and rough hands myself but not to fit in; that dirt was just a bitch to get out. I also became very fit too, very lean and strong indeed; we all did, lifting that awkward freight for hours every night was like getting a free full body workout that engaged every muscle. We worked hard together and for each other and became one of the top depots in the company for performance on freight shifted in the time limit and had the lowest delivering errors in the business; this was a result of those friendships. There was a great sense of belonging and community in our shift at that time and everybody bought into it. No one wanted to be a slack member of the team because they knew their friends would have to carry that slack.

After roughly six months I was offered a promotion by my line manager. Well, I say promotion — it wasn't really, that's just how they dressed it. There was no pay rise or even a contract to sign, but they wanted me to be a returns supervisor for the depot. It would be another part-time role added to the role I already had, so I would work from ten until four each day as the returns' supervisor and from four until eight (a couple hours reduced off the later shift) I would continue working with the part-time shift. I accepted their offer and started straight away. It wasn't a particularly pleasant job. In many ways you really did get the shit end of the company's stick in that area because you had to deal with many negative parts of the business. The unidentified freight being one, trying desperately to tie them into a short delivery load or find out where they come from, and if not, I then had to organise their sale at auction with head office. There was also damaged freight and that job mainly consisted of ringing customers to tell them their expensive package of rare wines or hand-painted, carefully crafted china vases had been obliterated by some idiot whacking a bloody big carpet on top of it and then asking them what they would like me to do with their box of now worthless junk while helping them file a claim and liaise with customer services. Most customers were actually quite polite and reasonable about the bad news; they saw it as a business and the insurance always covered the claim, but I would occasionally get the odd nutter suggesting where I could stick their broken glass. There was one bloke in particular even threatening to come down to the depot and make me eat what was left of the contents of his parcel. Despite the threats from angry callers who wanted to smash my face in, split bottles of chemicals containing God only knows what inside, smashed cutlery, broken wine bottles and unidentified tractor tyres that no one reported missing, I really enjoyed the challenge. I became very good at it too despite receiving little training and I always managed to clear my area of freight each day. I got to know a lot of the drivers over time as well as the office staff and really began to feel part of the whole family there. None of the staff, whether you were a porter or a line manager, earned a great deal of money, but we always managed to have a laugh and would always spend a few minutes of each day catching up, sharing stories and telling jokes over a cup of coffee in the morning. The next few years in that role were amazing. I was truly in my element working as part of a large and close team, but there was a problem. My problem was a depot manager by the name of Paul. He was a slimy, greasy, two-faced and arrogant piece of work. He stood just under six-foot tall, slim build, and he always had a completely shaven head that looked like he polished it every day. He always wore a blue shirt inside a grey suit jacket and he always wore a grin permanently slapped across his cocky-looking face. He walked around with a slight hunch, as if he'd spent his whole childhood slumped forward looking at his shoes and spoke like a low-paid cockney extra in a small budget British gangster movie. He always used to bang on about how hard he was because he'd come from a rough area in Croydon, so he grew up having to be tough because he was always getting into fights and scraps. Every day without fail there would be a story about his tough upbringing. I bet he never had a real fight in his bloody life! It didn't bother me too much. I mean, it was annoying and pure bullshit, but I could easily switch off when he opened his gob. I was never into all that macho stuff anyway, particularly when it was false and constant. I could only think he did it as a way of trying to impress the young ladies that worked on the phone in the traffic/drivers' office. He was supposed to be leading them and instead he was using his time to try and impress women who worked for him and judging by their awkward, silent reactions, one-word answers and bored expressions on their faces they thought exactly the same as me and couldn't wait for him to shut the hell up and leave the office. The only time he would put his little gangster persona away was when the General Manager or a director was in the building. Then his swagger quickly melted away and was replaced with a creepy, over-polite, tie-knot clutching sweat ball. I had no respect for him; he was just one of life's bullshitters, and you can find them in nearly every place of work and although it was annoying, I suppose it was harmless. What was getting under my skin was the way he was trying to micro-manage the job I'd been doing quite successfully for nearly three years at that point.

I ignored his self-interest, tolerated his lack of leadership, I even turned a blind eye at the times he would come up into my department and fill the boot of his car with brand new shoes and unclaimed wines that were supposed to be auctioned off, but what I couldn't stand was his interference in the running of my department, mainly because he didn't have a clue how to run it.

He was picking holes in me and my department for one reason and one reason only, his promotion.

You see, I never really had much to do with him directly. I had my shift manager called Chris who was a lovely bloke, very gently spoken, very humble and an absolute grafter who had worked his way up through the ranks from the bottom to get his position to act as a go-between. All my department dealings usually went through Chris. He was also responsible for my area as well as the part-time evening shift. He was someone I genuinely trusted to manage everyone and everything fairly. But Paul was beginning to take a direct interest in my area, bypassing Chris because Gary, the General Manager, was leaving the company and his position was up for grabs and Paul wanted it. The way Paul thought he could guarantee his promotion was by finding improvements in every department, including mine, straight after Gary left, making him appear to be a great interim manager and a strong candidate. But for some reason his micro-management seemed to evolve into an active dislike for me. I think it was because I was a young lad who stood his ground and Paul hated anyone he couldn't push straight over. Paul would do this thing where he would come up with a theory of why something wasn't working or why an area of the business was lagging, relying more on his imagination than the facts to produce his opinion; most would swallow his stupid theories but I didn't and he didn't like his authority being challenged. He started pulling me into his office over every little thing, like if a customer got angry and had spoken to me about his issues it was suddenly my fault he was angry, not the fact the lads had just broken thousands of pounds' worth of this guy's stock and he couldn't be calmed down as he'd lost his client from a failure to deliver. Nope, I was to blame because he wasn't satisfied with our claim procedures. Paul would complain about my area of the warehouse being messy, even though it was the tidiest area. He would state that I was lazy and complacent, but my area was clear, and I was doing everything I was supposed to do, my paperwork was up together, and I was working twelve-hour days. He was becoming insufferable because his opinions were completely warped.

Although I was always confident in the quality of work I did, a few months of daily run-ins with Paul, spats, confrontations and receiving constant criticisms I began to feel weighed down by it all. I just wanted to turn up and do my job, have a laugh at the same time with my colleagues and go home again. I loved where I worked, I got along with everybody but that was beginning to change. Because of weeks of being put down I was turning up and not talking to anybody. My self-esteem was getting lower, my confidence gradually eaten away, but I also thought if I kept my head down enough, I could slip underneath his radar, but it never worked. The only thing it did was just strain relationships I valued because I stopped joining in the chats and bonding. The place and the people I had become very fond of were being replaced by stress, negativity and misery.

One morning I got a phone call from one of the other returns' supervisors from our Ipswich depot. They'd normally give a courtesy call to let me know damaged freight was being returned to our Hampshire depot, but this time it was a call to let me know he was retiring and wanted to wish me all the best and let me know who his replacement would be. Naturally, I wished him good luck with his future plans and gave thanks for all the help he'd given me in the first couple of years, then, I can't remember exactly how, but the conversation turned to our salaries where he informed me that all the returns supervisors in the company were on a salary of around twenty-four thousand pounds a year. I was gobsmacked and totally embarrassed. I was so embarrassed that I remember lying on the phone to him. I made out that I was on the same salary as the rest of them to avoid the humiliation of admitting I was doing his job for a fraction of the wage. When the phone call ended, I didn't go anywhere or do anything for at least fifteen minutes while I tried to calm down the anger that was building inside me.

What an absolute piece of shit Paul was! Not only had he been constantly running me down for weeks and unfairly too, he was also trying to cut back on my hours even more by this point by saying too much time was being dedicated to my area, but now I'd discovered he'd undercut me massively right from the start by keeping me on five pound seventy-nine an hour, and it was a full-time position at every other depot, mine was only part time. It was all on him; he couldn't deny it because he'd spent three years reminding people that he was the one that paid our wages and negotiated our contracts almost daily. He'd set the price for my appointment, he'd ripped me off, then run me down over my efforts. Now, we could always argue that I should have negotiated better before I took the position, so ultimately, I was responsible for my agreed earnings, which would be a fair point, but you have to bear in mind at the time there were several other porters who were more than willing to do the job for that money, so I took it knowing I had a very weak negotiating position, plus I also believed the job was being fairly sold to me.

I never actually cared about the money on its own. It wouldn't have bothered me in the slightest if he had just kept his stupid cockney-imitating trap shut and left me alone. He was already getting really good value for money, but he continued pushing and pushing it to really rip me off, and I couldn't stand it.

I went to his office that afternoon and confronted him about it. I stayed cool and calm throughout his excuses. He said I never signed a contract as they were never sure if they were going to keep me on, that they weren't sure if I could adopt the role to a level they required, despite having three years to make their minds up and I was one of the best returns guys in the company in terms of results. Then, after all the months or arguing, putting me down and slagging me off to every other department about how much I was letting the depot down he had the cheek to tell me what a fantastic job I was doing despite our differences (him being the instigator) and what a valuable member of the team I was. Nothing but a cheap and shallow attempt to butter me up so he could tell me that I wouldn't be getting a pay rise as there was no money for it, but it was something he would definitely look into in the future.

From his point of view, to increase staff costing right at the point of his general manager's interview when he was trying so hard to impress the directors with cutbacks and efficiency could have blown his chances completely. In other words, I could go and whistle for what I actually deserved, or he could have actually paid me what he was supposed to in the beginning — then we wouldn't have been in this situation; it was his doing as far as I was concerned, but it was me that was going to be undercut again as a result.

There was no point arguing with him or protesting; he wasn't going to budge.

So a couple of days later I got up extra early, took the bus to town and signed on at a temp agency. I managed to secure a temp to perm contract working in a bank's processing centre dealing with cheques and account closures. The agency had just secured this deal with the bank and had more positions available than they did people on their books so they were practically throwing the contract at me, but the truth is I didn't want to leave, I wasn't ready to leave. I felt like I was walking away from my family. I was truly upset about going but I knew it had to be done on principle. If I had stayed, it would have only shown how weak I could be and leave the door of opportunity open for Paul to take advantage of me again in the future whenever he needed to. People like Paul only know how to push and take and as long as he remained in my workplace; the situation would always be there, and it would always be beyond my control.

I did, however, make sure the last laugh belonged to me. Because I was still on their part-time contract, I only had to give a week's notice whereas an office member or a supervisor on a full-time contract would have to provide a full working month. Paul was absolutely livid when I handed my notice in to him with only five working days stated in the letter. He was protesting, shouting at me and trying it on saying I should be giving a month as technically I was a member of the office staff and a supervisor, forgetting the week before he was trying to play that part of it down!

There was nothing in my contract legally to keep me there any longer than a week and I took great delight in telling him so. He ended the meeting by telling me that because of my unprofessional conduct and poor attitude with regard to my notice that I wouldn't be welcome back to the company as long as he was in charge there. I felt like saying fair enough and good riddance, but I had a bit more dignity than that, plus he'd also done me a favour in a way. I knew no matter how bad things got, I couldn't go crawling back to him with my tail between my legs. I worked the full weeks' notice, and I started at the bank's process centre the following Monday, leaving just before his big general manager's interview and also leaving him without a supervisor. He did manage to get the job despite my little spanner in the works, but it was short lived. Six months into the new role he was sacked for fraudulent behaviour. To stop the depot having to pay transfer fees to local agencies supplying him decent night shift workers Paul would tell those workers to hand in their notices at the agency, wait a couple of weeks and he would employ them directly. The agency found out and contacted the head office up near Nottingham. They came down and sacked him on the spot the next day, they even had security staff in there to supervise him while he cleared his desk out, and all this was told to me by the customer service ladies I bumped into on a work night out a couple of weeks after it happened. As for the returns' supervisor role? He had to take someone on and offer them full salary and invest in their training.

## Office and computer skills

My next employment was, of course, at the bank's processing centre. It wasn't just any old processing centre, it was the headquarters for their nationwide customer services team, whoop whoop! Exciting stuff! It also dealt with all postal account queries including bonds, ISAs, cheque withdrawals, account openings and closures for the whole country and it was a huge operation.

The bank owned one of the biggest, smartest and most modern buildings in the town, complete with a fully furnished gym, hotel rooms for travelling company executives, tennis courts, five-a-side football pitches, a bar and a spa, and they employed well over six hundred local people in various different roles and it all looked very professional indeed.

I remember being very nervous. I'd never worked in a proper office before. My old office was a large cage I sat in at the end of the warehouse and it was also used as a lockup at night to secure the unmarked freight. I'd used computers before in the last job, but they were internal programmes specifically designed for the company and the system was very outdated. I had very limited knowledge of modern computers and knew next to nothing about the banking world except how to empty my bank account rapidly straight after pay day. Despite all my disadvantages, I still had enough confidence to back myself in being able to adapt to any problems put before me, but no amount of self-belief or confidence could have prepared me for the environment I was about to face. It may have looked extremely professional on the surface but internally it was filled to the brim with arse kissers, creeps, two-faced liars, creeps and back stabbers, and did I mention creeps? It was, and still is, one of the strangest working environments I've ever been exposed to. It felt more like I unknowingly joined some sort of brainwashed cult rather than alternative employment; it was unbelievable to watch. They were people I assumed to be decent, reasonable people, free thinking members of our society that would go to this place of work, but as soon as they walked through the dark glass entrance where nobody from the outside world could see them, they became some of the slimiest people I've ever encountered. Most of them would talk openly at their desks about the best ways to suck up to their supervisors, giving tips and methods on how to win their bosses' favour and be noticed by them as if it was a completely normal thing to do at work. And the supervisors themselves? They lapped it all up, never questioning such behaviour, they couldn't get enough of sickly over-complimenting and the cheap, shitty little office gifts that bore no class or sentiment. Everybody in that building was fake. Everybody that I spoke to more or less admitted they were different people at work from the people they were at home. Approaching all colleagues with big, sweet smiles or their lips puckered up for the boss's behind while at the same time holding a razor-sharp knife behind their back at all times. It was a cringy, awkward and pathetic environment where everybody wanted to get ahead in the promotion game and they didn't give two shits how low they sunk morally at the chance to be recognised as a "somebody" in that world. Team meetings consisted of young, smartly dressed workers gathered tightly around a marker board in the morning being asked questions about the latest business buzzwords by a slightly higher twat and the "sheeple" would shoot their hands up in the air as fast as they could like children in a primary school class bursting to be the one who could answer the teacher's questions in an effort to demonstrate how brilliant and brainwashed, they were. It was all to desperately win the acceptance and approval of somebody who struggled to even remember their names.

The minutes and days would be forever filled with coffee and muffins brought to the manager that they never really liked or wanted. Delivered with the same put on, slightly over the top smile, while simultaneously fake laughing at the boss's stupid "dad" joke and trying to find another ten-second window in which to impress them with how much they'd recently learned and reminding their employer how much they loved being in the job. If you kept any decency or self-respect with you past the entrance to the building, then you had to have a sick bucket with you at all times or make sure you were heavily medicated to deal with the amount of nausea you were likely to experience. I'd never worked with people like this before, I'd never known people like this before. Don't get me wrong, you will always find the company suck-up wherever you go, that's just the way it goes; it's almost like a business policy, a social position that just has to be filled by somebody to complete the dynamic of a working environment, but it's normally always one, two at the very most per company. At the processing centre it was a second language and every employee seemed to be fluent in it. They were the best I'd seen at it too because they didn't seem to carry an ounce of shame about their behaviour, they embraced it, and then normalised it.

I remember asking myself at the time, is this what all office environments are like?

I remember as a kid walking home from school, having to cut through the town centre each day to get back and I would see all these young men and women that come from this building in their suits, smart dresses or skirts, looking very professional and I used to think they must be quite successful. They've got office jobs, that means they've got good jobs, secure jobs. They've got power, money, responsibility and they're on the right track to more of it and a secure future. Turning up to this centre and being on the inside of it I realised the lie we all force upon ourselves through appearance on a daily basis. Presenting an image of a working world that doesn't exist. All these smart-looking people I passed on the street as a young boy had no power, they made no real money and they weren't successful. They were nothing more than porters, waiters and servants, demanded to dress a little better than their manual working counterparts really, working for the same crappy, low end wages that can barely keep a roof over their heads, and the only difference is, some of them bought into the lie and thought a job like that automatically made them better people than those that work in warehouses or on shop floors for the same money.

I worked every day there under the radar. I never spoke to anybody I didn't have to, and I refused to join the deeply established butt-licking cult that consumed the entire workforce. I just kept my head down and got on with my work. I did manage to make two friends while I was there, and funnily enough, the immediate common ground we all found was believing we were the only sane people inside this corporate religion. The rest of them I actively shut out on a personal level because I had no respect for them.

There were two brilliant perks that come with the job. The first was free, hot drink vending machines on every floor of the building that you could visit as often as you wanted. It was never questioned even if you went up there twenty times a day. The caffeine keeps you alert and made you more productive; who was I to turn down the benefits of their productivity strategy? The second, because I didn't have to face or speak to a customer as all I did was process, I could use headphones at my desk the whole day, meaning I could completely drown out the world around me and just focus on what I was there to do.

After about six months into the job, the department manager came and got me from my workstation for a chat in his office. Which I must admit got me a little nervous because I thought it was going to be a "your face doesn't quite fit and we've got to let you go" speech but to my surprise, it wasn't.

He actually liked the fact I came in and got on with the work, that I never looked to be noticed and that I set a good example to my colleagues. He then asked if I would be willing to accept a role as a subject consultant (their way of saying team leader basically, without having to pay the same). I would receive a permanent contract and then go on a probationary period of three months as a consultant and they would review the position after that time and if I performed well, it would be a promotion. I couldn't believe it; it was great news because it restored a little of my faith back in the workplace, being one of the few that kept their self-respect and was offered a position on merit, not the way I puckered up.

I worked very hard in the role, determined to prove my worth, always helping the team, motivating them at the morning brief instead of passing out new buzz words to remember, staying behind to help and train others while holding up a clear, zero tolerance to anyone who tried to win me over with flattery or trying to suck up to me. Whenever I had spare time, I worked with them processing bonds to set a good example and show that the real work of the business was never going to be beneath me.

It all worked too. Within a few months we had one of the best teams on the floor, producing some of the highest processing figures in the department and it was achieved through creating a positive no-nonsense environment, I didn't need to take a single thing away or make a threat or even raise my voice once. I emphasised teamwork and development and together as a group of twenty, we were all performing at our best.

The time arrived to talk about my new contract and so my line manager and the regional director Mike (who loved to refer to himself in the third person constantly) called me in for a meeting.

"First of all, I want to start by saying what a fantastic job you've done with the team."

"Thanks, Tim."

"They are performing better than ever before, we're retaining more staff in the department, which means less turnover and less time and money spent on training and you have been a massive part of that improvement."

"Thanks," my confidence dropping as I began to anticipate the "but".

"But unfortunately, we're not going to be offering you a promotion at this time."

"I see, can I ask why?"

"It's nothing you've done, you've produced some excellent results but the department is going to be downsizing due to branch closures and the economic downturn and we've had to let some people go to stay in line with the business need."

"Right."

"I'll be moving on to manage another department and Haley, a manager whose team has just been released by the company will be coming in to take over my role and she'll be bringing her own subject consultant Suzie with her."

"I see."

I sat right back in the chair clearly looking disappointed before Mike added, "You've shown real promise in the role over the past few months, mate, and Tim and I are both now very confident in your abilities and potential and when a new role emerges, your name will be one of the first put forward for it."

"Thank you very much, Mike, I'm gutted, of course. but it is what it is, thanks."

What else could I say or do? It was just bad timing, sod's law. I couldn't blame anybody there for the situation the company and the country were in. Sometimes that's just the way life goes. Timing is everything. I understood at that moment they needed to resource the managers they already possessed rather than let them go and spend money training up somebody new. Still, as gutted as I felt it wasn't the end of the world, I could go back to processing. I'd secured my job at ground level and I was extremely grateful for that, knowing others in the same area had been let go. I could return back to my original role, pressure-free working, headphones plugged in and living in my own bubble, or so I thought.

I'm not entirely sure what happened to Suzie the new consultant in the weeks that followed her move, but she really put the pressure on me. I can only guess that she was put under a bit of pressure herself, from those above (Mike), to improve on her performance as a leader or someone else (me) would be able to step into the role if she couldn't.

I guessed this because every day after joining the team she singled me out personally. Shouting at me over the most trivial errors that everybody made daily. If something wasn't done, completed or missed, it was my name yelled out for everybody to hear and whenever I asked why I was singled out above everyone else for the mistakes that others were making she would say I was the senior member of the team (made up title with no extra pay) and I should know better. How could I possibly be responsible for what Kay, the old dear on the team, had missed in her processing pile at the other end of our office over fifty feet away? It just didn't make any sense, but then again, I suppose it didn't have to. It was the pressure that counted, not the substance of the argument itself, and it worked too. Every morning I walked in with nerves, anxiety and fear. Fear she would slither up behind me at any moment and begin shouting in my ear for the whole team to hear and making me jump with her thick Irish accent and bad breath consisting of coffee, cigarettes and shit flavoured toothpaste. I tried so hard to ignore her as best as I could, but she wouldn't leave me alone. I tried to talk to Haley about what was happening, but nothing was done about it.

As much as I got along with Haley and found her a very approachable manager, she and Suzie had worked together well over ten years, they were the only two people to come over from the old team and that made Suzie probably one of the only people Haley felt she could trust and in a backstabbing environment like ours, it must have been a rare thing.

It went on and on for weeks until one Friday morning I reached my limit. A whole pile of cheques had been put through onto the system under the wrong sort code and account number. Everybody in the team had done it, everybody should have been to blame because no one spotted it until it was too late, but I was singled out once again. I was blamed for not spotting the mistake, even though it was her responsibility to check the work before it went out, not mine, and I was given no such instruction to do it. As soon as she finished bawling at me right in the middle of the office for the whole department to witness, she stormed off to inform Haley what had happened, probably spinning some shit as to how it was my fault and not hers but I didn't stick around to find out. I very calmly sat down and logged out of my computer, I packed up my little metal desk/locker drawer to the side of my workstation and I walked out, no warning, no threats, no dramas or any fuss at all — you'd have thought I was nipping out to lunch or an appointment if you hadn't witnessed what had taken place moments before. I went straight from there to a work agency ten minutes' walk away in the town centre and was signed onto their books right away. By the Monday I was working and didn't miss out on a day's pay.

They hadn't noticed my disappearance for nearly three and a half hours! And apparently the team were too scared to tell Suzie what had happened, so they just sat there and waited for her to put it together herself.

When they finally did notice, Haley phoned me and tried to persuade me to come back and talk it through with her but by then it was too late. After weeks of anxiety and unfair, unnecessary stress and mixed with the fact I had secured alternative employment straight away I felt liberated. No matter what they offered, which wasn't very much, I just couldn't go back and face one single moment more in the presence of a deeply insecure woman who projected her pressures and fears onto me unfairly; plus, her breath was driving me bonkers even when she wasn't shouting at me.

Haley left about a year later to go and manage a pub with her new partner after a huge dispute at work with Suzie. Turns out the old hag with shit for breath couldn't be trusted after all. Suzie had made numerous complaints about Haley's management style and conduct. When Haley found out she couldn't stomach her long-term work pal any longer and left. Suzie stepped into her job straight away.

# Chapter Four
# Work experience (2)

## Agency (various roles)

For roughly the next year after the processing centre, I was on the temp books with one of the town's employment agencies. The staff that run it were polite and friendly enough people that always greet you with a warm and welcoming smile when you walked into their professional but relaxed office environment where you were encouraged and motivated to get out there and seize opportunities. As charming as all that sounds, it didn't mean for a moment they were decent or genuine people, though, and they certainly weren't stupid either.

I'd put on my application form that I was looking for temp to perm work only, just like most people did who went in, but they still required workers to pick up the odds and sods of the jobs they had promised to cover for companies who only needed an extra pair of hands for a short space of time.

I spent the coming months getting calls like "now I know it's not temp to perm like you've asked for but it's just something in the meantime until we find you a place" or "now we're in the process of securing you a possible temp to perm position but what you could do for me in the time being". They already had temp to perm places, loads of them. Contracts with some large and local companies with dozens of vacancies to fill but they were reserved for friends or friends of friends first. Or those who played the temp game long enough. I had to play the game too and earn my spot; they couldn't admit this was the case, of course, but I had to tidy up all their bits of crap that came through the door first before I'd be rewarded with a shot at a bit of job security. The temp jobs I did receive at that time were pretty consistent, to be fair to the agency. I probably averaged a four-day week most weeks but the jobs they had me doing weren't exactly desirable, and why would they be? Some of the jobs were deliberately pushed externally from companies because no sucker within their organisation wanted to do them. I had little choice, I had to pay my dues to get back into a secure environment.

I spent a few weeks at a salad company on the edge of Hampshire working on a production line. My job was to stand at the very end of the line with my rubber gloved hands and I would stick them into each salad pot that passed me on the conveyor belt and "fluff" up the contents inside the bowl in an effort to make it appear as though there was more salad in the bowl than there actually was. What a piece of shit, dishonest and boring job that was, a salad fluffer and lettuce customer deceiver! They'd rather pay someone to try and rip off the customers over the contents of their mixed salad packs than stick a couple of extra lettuce leaves in, what a complete fucking joke, embarrassing. I felt sorry for the poor sods who worked there, I really did. It was so loud, too loud to speak over the machines churning away, too loud for conversation to take place and no headphones were allowed for obvious hygiene reasons, meaning there were no distractions; you couldn't escape the reality of your job or the humming and grinding of all the machines in a refrigerated environment.

The fifteen-minute breaks they gave you seemed almost completely pointless. By the time you got to the dressing room, removed the hairnets, gloves, boots, took off your overcoat, changed into your own shoes, washed your hands and walked to the canteen you had about four minutes left before you had to turn around and get all that crap back on to begin work again, so unless you were able to swallow the contents of a freshly boiled kettle it was pointless trying to get a cup of tea as you were not allowed to take it back in with you. I was on the minimum wage doing that job, but it was the agency I worked for that set my pay. The permanent staff there were actually on very good money to compensate for their limited working conditions and I was told by the supervisors I too should have been suitably compensated by the agency for the same reason, as the company had paid a lot of money for me and a few others to be there and wanted to provide incentive for the conditions, but the agency kept all the extra dosh they were given and dished out the bare minimum instead.

When my time at the salad company had finished, I was moved over to landscape gardening for a month to go and work for a local but rather successful company where the owner had a reputation of being an absolute arsehole. The workload was huge too, it was fast paced and hard going. Every task, even something like planting a small tree had to be performed with the utmost intensity; anything less was considered slacking. The owner was determined to squeeze every drop of energy from his workforce and his temp staff and if he couldn't, they wouldn't be there long, and if the temps took a single day sick, even because of a work-related injury, they wouldn't come back.

The agencies hated dealing with him because he called pretty much daily to complain about the standard of staff being supplied to him (which were not bad at all) but rather than the agencies refusing to do business with such a difficult person with ridiculously high standards they took his money every time knowing they were sending people into a very poor environment with an impossible employer for a bit of commission.

I did enjoy the work itself, gravelling drives, planting shrubs on school grounds during the term times and tarmacking pathways. It was outdoors, physical and hands on and I could have stayed on past a few months despite the employer's attitude towards his staff, but after I witnessed a certain incident I refused to go back there.

One evening I returned to the company depot to unload the van after spending all day cutting hedges and strimming on college grounds to find the depot manager stood in the middle of the yard screaming into a young lad's face and I mean screaming — he couldn't have been any louder if he tried. The manager's face could only have been inches from this young lad's, who must have been in his late teens (and in need of a decent feed) and this young lad was shaking from head to toe with fear and I didn't blame him, I'd have been scared too; it was very intimidating. He was clearly frightened of the much older, taller and larger man and, of course, embarrassed too, as everyone who was in the yard began to gather around and watch. I remember thinking he must have done something very serious for such a confrontation; maybe he had caused some considerable damage to a property in some way or hurt someone with a reckless act to justify such a dressing down, but as the rant unfolded, I discovered it was because the young temp was ten minutes late getting into work. Ten minutes! Oh, my goodness, quick! Get the fucking firing squad ready! It was unbelievable. The manager shouting about how he had then made the whole team late for work as they were sat around waiting for him. The whole thing was ridiculous. The young lad could have had a genuine reason why he was late, but he didn't give one when he turned up that morning. He was too frightened to tell the boss he'd been late (unsurprisingly), so instead someone on his crew had grassed him up when he got back to the depot. I was so angry because the young lad had been humiliated in front of twenty odd strangers and was trying his best to hold back tears forming in his eyes and looked one good shake away from wetting himself. Adrenaline coursed through my body witnessing such an unnecessary act of aggression. Before I could step in the depot manager stormed off and started slamming tools around in the yard and the young lad walked straight out but I wasn't prepared to leave it there. The next morning, I refused to go to work. I texted the agency, telling them I wouldn't be going in and instead, I went straight down the agency's office to make a formal complaint about the manager's behaviour in the hope something would be done about it. Of course, I should have been more realistic and expected the "we'll look into it" speech, which is exactly what I ended up getting. The agency still took the owner's money and they still sent people to him to be treated like shit and they had absolutely no care for resolving the bullying of the young staff they sent in to get it, they were on commission and that was all they cared about. My complaint was logged, but it was very quickly swept under the carpet.

I spent the next five to six months after that installing and repairing garage doors as a fitter's mate alongside a Hungarian guy by the name of Zoltan who I got along with really well. The garage door depot had a very large customer radius which meant we travelled along most of southern England and parts of Wales doing various jobs and it was brilliant. Every day was something different in terms of the places and the challenges. I would have loved to have stayed with them, but unfortunately the company were relocated to Southampton and were downsizing their operation, meaning Zoltan was out of a permanent job and I found myself looking for work once more.

My next placement was at a factory that made cleaning and sterilising machines for hospitals, which sounds very complex and technical if I were actually working on those machines. Instead, they gave me a far more important job! They were relocating and downsizing as well, so they were having a massive clear-out that was overdue by about fifty years and I was the guy they hired to clean out all their crap.

Every department from customer services down to the foreman's office were being gutted out and had to be reduced in size and storage by over fifty percent. I removed all the rubbish from each department and dumped it at the back of the building. Then I had to sort through all the rubbish into metals, plastics, paper, then sling it all into the appropriate skip. You'd think such a job wouldn't last very long, how much rubbish could one building or business have? Well, the company was over a hundred years old and had documents stored in their loft spaces and cupboards going back that far, so the job lasted a good, few months. I didn't mind it at all; it was outdoors for half the day, I was trusted to get on and work on my own and I got three breaks a day, including an hour for lunch and my pay sat just above the minimum hourly rate. I didn't mind the grubby conditions or even the giant rats that ran between the different skips throughout the day, but it wasn't exactly long-term job security. The company liked my work rate and my attitude, so they asked if I could stay on longer to help them with the move to help them set up in their new location on the opposite side of town which lasted a couple more months, but when that came to an end, they couldn't offer me anything permanent. They expressed they would have liked to, which was always nice to hear, but they had downsized to a location a little bit tighter for space than they expected and were even talking about letting some of their production staff go and outsourcing some of their work as they no longer had the room to accommodate.

During all this time I had been asking the agency if any temp to perm jobs had come through. "Still nothing, I'm afraid, we will keep looking in the meantime..." In other words, I was too valuable to them cleaning up the crap that was coming in through the door and they couldn't rely on anyone else to do it, so I had to sit tight.

My next assignment after that was helping two caretakers with a big moving job at the local college. Two of the county's colleges were merging together to make just one slightly bigger college managed on a smaller budget with more classrooms being built to cope with the influx of students in one location. My job was to move books, bookshelves, chairs, tables, boxes and anything else that fills a classroom to newly built areas and I spent every minute of my working day lifting and clocking up the miles walking. Again, I quite liked it; it was basic manual work, it didn't tax the brain, so my mind would wander off and pretend I was somewhere else, never having to concentrate too much on the task in hand. I got a decent amount of break time and a strong cup of coffee to get me going made by one of the college staff every morning and the best thing about it: there were no self-important idiots to report to every day either; it was an all-right job. There were, however, two problems that came with this little short-term assignment. The first issue I had was the two caretakers. Shortly before I arrived, they were given the responsibility and training in providing the light, general security for the college grounds and they were also provided with basic handheld radios with which to contact each other and you'd have thought they'd suddenly been asked to guard the Prime Minister the way they banged on about it. On and on nine hours a day I'd listen to them talk about the risks and dangers they could face if a situation occurred in our sleepy, rural town in Hampshire where nothing ever happens. It was like Rambo didn't have a patch on their "war" stories, trespassers and people cutting through the grounds to save time on their journeys into the town, nothing was too big for these guys to handle! I tried sticking my headphones in to drown them out, but they didn't take the hint and instead just talked at me, forcing me to politely engage in their verbal waffle. The second problem I had was the college building I was temping at was directly opposite the bank's processing centre I had walked out of; only sixteen feet of road separated the two properties.

When I walked out of that place about a year before, I wanted them to think I was walking off into better career prospects and opportunities. It didn't necessarily have to be true, just them not knowing what had become of me was enough to feel like I'd taken the win from that situation, but that was blown to bits after the first day in my new role at half past four when they all walked out of the building in their smart dresses and shirts to see me lumping around ageing school furniture in my own shabby work jeans and a ripped shirt with the two "bodyguards" right behind me with nothing in their hands but radios. The whole scenario made it look as though I was completing my community service and they were there to ensure I didn't steal anything. Nearly everyone from my old team at the bank saw me but they were too embarrassed to come up and say anything to me, but I knew it would be all around their office the next day. Don't get me wrong, I wasn't ashamed of my circumstances at all. I was a young working man trying to earn an honest living and nobody should ever be ashamed of that, no matter what they do. I just didn't want to give my old team or Suzie the satisfaction of thinking somehow in their little bubbles I'd dropped to a place lower than them. The reality was, as I stood there in my old rugby top and faded jeans watching them come out of their building, I had more freedom than they did, I wasn't trapped in the same place day after day and I could be myself, I didn't have to change who I was to survive. It did, however, remind me that I'd spent long enough in the temping gig and if the agency weren't going to find me a permanent position, I'd have to find one myself. I was sorting out their temp placements well and leaving behind a good reputation for them and because of that the agency was in no rush to change my position. I had to start looking outside the agencies.

I spotted a job vacancy one weekend in the local paper. It was a supervisor's role for a company just outside the town that delivered all kinds of spraying chemicals and different fertilisers to farms all over the south from a tiny little warehouse that had been converted from a barn a farmer rented out to the business right out in the countryside. They delivered chemicals so small but expensive at times you could drive through three counties over just to deliver something the size of a soda can. My job would be to load the vehicles with these "soda cans" and other bottles, plan routes for up to eight different drivers, store and log the stock that comes into the barn/warehouse and occasionally go out and deliver myself. It sounded like a great opportunity, so I called them and managed to secure myself an interview for the following week. I was nervous but felt as though the interview went well and sure enough, they phoned back the afternoon of my interview to tell me they were very impressed with the way I'd handled it and offered me the position. I was thrilled, of course, but it came with a slight catch. Because of my lack of qualifications for the role they didn't want to offer me the full eighteen thousand pound a year the job was originally advertised for and instead wanted to offer me fifteen thousand a year. It wasn't their fault, but given my past experiences I was tired of being stooped over money, so I decided to be a bit firmer with my negotiating this time. Worst case scenario, they refused to negotiate, I stayed on the temp books a bit longer and started the job hunt again; I had nothing to lose. I was asked to go in and meet with them once more to discuss the terms. By the end of the meeting, we had reached an agreement we were all happy with. I would start on the fifteen thousand pounds. If I passed my basic course, forklift test and attained my ADR license I would get the pay rise up to eighteen at my first employee's review in a year's time.

The job was great, and it was also seasonal work. During the winter months, hardly anything went out the doors for delivery. Self-employed drivers we contracted in would cut back to about four as the deliveries dropped right off. I would start my morning at seven every day, plan routes for each driver, load them up, take in deliveries and be done by ten o'clock. It was so easy, too easy in fact during the quieter months I was encouraged by members of the office and sales team who resided in a portacabin next to the barn to kill time by playing computer games with them, but that wasn't for me. Instead, I made use of my time by cleaning out the barn/warehouse toilets and giving it a fresh coat of paint and installing a new door I'd built myself. I painted the whole warehouse floor, re-organised all the stock to make the popular products more accessible and the least popular pushed to the back on the higher storage. I got that warehouse twice as efficient from when I first started, and I took a little pride in that.

In the summer months it got a little busier. They warned me in the interview that the orders would suddenly explode at that time of year and I would be rushed off my feet. It definitely got a lot busier but certainly nothing to get too excited about. The drivers went out full and I occasionally had to make a few deliveries myself but certainly nothing drastic. By the end of the season, they had informed me that as a depot and a nationwide company we had one of the busiest and most successful years in its history. I couldn't believe it. I'd hardly broken a sweat. Maybe it was because the warehouse was now so well organised or maybe it was because the managers that warned me didn't really know what hard work was, but I remember thinking to myself if that was as busy as it got here, I'd have nothing to worry about. I really enjoyed the work and the responsibility that came with it. I was a young man in his early twenties in charge of many drivers over twice my age and that was not something I'd allowed to go to my head like others would. I had to remain humble and respectful, remembering their time in the job and their life experience trumped mine, so it was always best to listen to them and take their advice on board because they knew best and I never ever talked at them. I would have definitely struggled if I'd cut them off with arrogance; not only that but imposing my own limited view and ignoring experience just isn't leadership.

The holiday was good there, over twenty days plus bank holidays and they were always good with granting holiday providing it wasn't right in the middle of the busy season. I could manage my own breaks, which I did, but never felt the need to take half of them because I wasn't having to escape any micro-managing penises, I'd eat my lunch at the desk while I was working or given my surroundings I occasionally elected to go walking in the countryside if the weather was nice and take in the stunning views of fields and forestry around me; it was right on my doorstep after all.

There were only two problems (as before) with the job. One of the office staff really didn't like me. A man in his forties called Andrew, not Andy but Andrew! He was the purchasing manager for the depot. Always in some old, thick and groovy woolly jumper or pinstriped shirt, he would constantly peer over his ridiculously small spectacles to speak down to me in a stupidly over-snobby voice as if he was a headmaster at a public school from the nineteen fifties. I wasn't being paranoid. He didn't address anybody else like that, just me. He obviously felt he had the right to look down his nose at me. Why, I don't know, maybe it was because I was considerably younger than everyone else in the office. Or maybe it was the fact I was brought up on a council estate and not rural

Berkshire like he was. Cricket, church fetes, cucumber sandwiches and snobbery coursed through his veins whereas cheap cola and ham sandwiches and penny sweets coursed through mine. I was always polite and tried to speak well, carry myself confidently but that clearly wasn't enough to shake off the smell of the social housing I was brought up in. Did I mention he was the chairman of his local parish council? No, well he did, at least ten times a day. He was always taking care of his extra rural-related business during office hours, which wouldn't have bothered me if he didn't keep mentioning his bloody title in the twenty phone calls, he made every day, "It's Andrew, chairman of the parish council!" Get over yourself, man! They know who you are, you spoke to them yesterday and you mentioned it then! That on its own wasn't enough to put me off the job, of course. He was also the "pettyweight" champion of the world. He would do things like deliberately hide order sheets and delivery notes around the office that I had printed out so when I couldn't find them the next morning and began to seem on the verge of incompetent, he would rummage around and find them in the nick of time like some sort of office hero and appear as though me and the office couldn't function without him. How do I know this? Because one of the office admin ladies by the name of Ali saw him move the sheets repeatedly and told me, and he always put them in filing trays I never touched or went near — they belonged to my manager, not me, so I had no need to use them; I had my own desk. His whole life in the portacabin seemed to be job justification because in reality he didn't really do anything. He'd have to order one or two pallets of chemicals a day or sometimes per week in the colder months which took all of about ten minutes to do and therefore had to be seen as useful in other areas of the business even at the expense of trying to make others look foolish in case his superiors finally caught on to just how minimal his "really important role" was. All this wasn't the end of the world, of course, I mean it was bloody annoying being made to look foolish to the rest of the team on occasion, but I just stayed out of his way as best as I could, spending as much time in the warehouse or on the road and the least amount of time in the cabin.

The second problem I had was the bloody alarm system they had installed. Because I lived the closest (all the other staff coming from an old depot near Reading 50 miles away) they asked if I could be a point of contact for the alarm company in the event the system was triggered; no problem, happy to help. More responsibility would certainly add to my employee review in the coming months. I was only fifteen minutes' drive away, so I was the logical choice. About six months into the job as we were entering into the busy period there was a problem with one of the sensors in the warehouse's alarm system and they couldn't seem to fix it despite the engineer's repeated attempts and best efforts. I was being called out nearly every night of the week, weekends included, sometimes up to three times a night. Which doesn't sound like much, but I would be woken at all hours of the night, three, four, five in the morning, I'd have to get dressed, drive the fifteen minutes to the premises, unlock the gates, open up the portacabin, turn all the outside lighting on, wait for the police or fire brigade, depending on which alarm went off, open up the warehouse, let them inspect the property, turn all the lights back off, lock everything up and drive home and text my line manager to let them know I was dealing with it. Like I said I was doing that three times a night on occasion and each callout would take between an hour to an hour and a half each time and it got so bad it was happening almost every night. I was shattered going into work the following days. I never got the time back in lieu either. I never got to finish early or receive a bonus or callout fee. My petrol wasn't even being covered despite only earning fifteen grand a year and two other people were on the alarm company's contact list, but I was the only one doing it. Whenever I mentioned being called out several times in the night it almost created an awkward atmosphere amongst the staff in the cabin because they could clearly see I was absolutely exhausted from being up most of the night and in need of a good sleep but if they let me go home to rest, it would have meant them having to pitch in on the warehouse side of things and no one wanted to do it; they weren't cut out for it. So, they would sit there and listen and take it all in and say nothing. I didn't make a big thing of it, though, I took their lack of willingness to help on the chin, I only mentioned the callouts when I had to, so it could be recorded with head office and it would eventually be sorted, I'd hoped, plus my review was coming up at that time and I didn't want anything negative to spoil it. I had passed all the tests they had put me on within the first five months, I'd restructured the warehouse, always got the deliveries out well in time and I never had a return of failure. The warehouse was spotless, all admin and log books were up to date and I was going the extra mile with this callout crap too. Surely nothing was going to stand in my way, was it?

The employee reviews came around and my line manager Liam took me into the side office of the portacabin to go through it. It was an excellent review. I didn't put a toe out of line. The review said I went above and beyond, displayed a very positive and professional attitude and built a strong rapport with the drivers and some of the local customers and I was a valued member of the team, brilliant! Well done, me! But they weren't willing to give me the agreed pay rise. "Why not?"

"Given the current economic climate we're in the company cannot justify providing a pay increase at this time."

"They've just had their most successful financial year!"

"Yes… they have, but they're forecasting another downturn over the next three years with the financial uncertainty and recession, so they won't be putting through any pay increases for the foreseeable future."

"That's not what was agreed, Liam, I've worked really hard and done everything that was asked of me."

"I do know, and I'm sorry, you're a fantastic worker and a valued member of the team and if it was up to me, you'd have it but it's not, unfortunately, this has come from head office."

"Why say something if you can't keep your word?" Years of frustration from other jobs were finally coming to the surface and being let go into that meeting. My composure was dropping, and my patience had worn thin.

"Look, we didn't see the economic downturn coming and now it's here we have to react to it and prepare for it as a business as best we can," Liam said, getting firmer with his tone.

"Yes, you did! I came here during the economic downturn, Liam, which is when you offered these terms."

"Look, I'm sorry if you feel you've been cheated in some way but we can't budge on this issue, unfortunately, the way things are we're all lucky to be in a job without the threat of redundancy, and a pay rise will not be coming any time soon and let's face it, mate, you didn't get it in writing."

"What's that supposed to mean? We agreed on it in my interview, Liam, and we shook hands on it, isn't that supposed to mean something?"

"Like I said I'm sorry, mate, it's out of my hands, you are more than welcome to take this further with head office if you need to but they will only repeat what I've told you here."

I didn't say anything else. My usual politeness to say something neutralising to rid the room of awkward confrontation had escaped me that day. I no longer cared for politeness. I stood from my seat and left the little makeshift office.

I was angry, really fucking pissed off actually and did well to keep my cool as well as I had done. I really thought I'd done well to negotiate that time and not simply roll over on the terms. I should have got it in writing, but then again if I insisted on that they may have thought I wasn't worth that kind of hassle and just picked another candidate or thought I was stupid or untrusting for asking, not exactly employable traits. Although I take full responsibility for my own situation, I couldn't help but feel frustrated. There might not have been anything in writing, but they shook my hand and gave me their word and that should have been enough or failing that an apology would have got them halfway back. Your word is your bond, my grandad would always tell me, it's all you have, so never go back on it and never say you'll do something unless you're going to see it through. Now you might think I'm old school in my thinking as the world seems to rely and survive on the technicality of laws and contracts these days, but it's still important. It tells me morally who you are and what you're capable of and ultimately if I can trust you. I couldn't trust any of them. All those months of hard work and improvements and they let me down. It was easier for my manager to go against my pay increase than actually fight to see through what he'd promised.

I didn't hang around. The very next day I handed in my months' notice, kept my head down and got out of there. As expected, there were no farewells, no see-off pint down the road in the local pub to wish me all the best. I think they were too embarrassed. I left because they couldn't live up to their word or even try to, and if they did feel a little ashamed because of that, then good, it was deserved. I hope it made them think twice about making promises they couldn't keep to people who depended on those promises; might not have been intentional on their part, but the end result was a low blow.

Just over a year after I left, the company was bought up and incorporated into a larger chemical distribution company with a more efficient depot near Hampshire already. Most of the team were made redundant and the few that survived the cull had to relocate to a depot back towards Berkshire. I never saw or heard from any of them again.

# Chapter Five
# Work experience (3)

Training and use of machines and power and tools

While working my notice at the chemical farm place I immediately returned to the job hunt. It was at this particular time that all the different job hunt/CV sites were popping up online and on the tele. Where you typed in all your qualifications and experience and they found the most ideal jobs available for you based on the details you provided. It was new, exciting and efficient and no good for me. I had no real qualifications past GCSE really, and the only experience I had was in lifting various objects and a bit of driving. Not exactly enough to fill the website's pages with interest, it could barely fill a post note! Plus, the jobs on these sites seemed to be way out of my league and very, very, specific roles. As I scrolled down through each site, most of the jobs required qualifications that I didn't even know existed. The working world seemed to be exploding with all different kinds of new diplomas and university degrees and I didn't have any. I was getting quite scared of the working world moving on without me. I dreaded the idea of going back on the agency books for at least another year until they finished exploiting my work-rate, so I went back to the paper advertisements instead to find work more suitable to my non-academic achievements!

For three weeks I sifted through all the local rags and all the advertisements in the shop windows of the town centre; only they all appeared to be taken by well-qualified psychic job hunters who seemed to secure the position before the company had time to finish pinning the advertisement onto the glass. The odd one that was still vacant said experience required or essential. Oh, I'm sorry, I thought I was applying for a shop assistant role not heart surgeon's, not being funny but how much experience in that role is bloody essential? And that you can't pass on in training? How the hell do you ever get experience at the most basic employee level unless somebody is willing to give you the experience? Some people must be born with all the experience required or sales training needed, and I was just unfortunate in not possessing the auto-qualification gene.

I was on the verge of giving up any hope and beginning to think I was truly falling behind in the market. Then, one day away from phoning the agency, beginning to play out the phone call in my head, my older brother rang to put an unexpected opportunity my way.

He was heading off back to London to move in with his long-term girlfriend and also begin a new career working in the city, and his old job was up for grabs. For the four years previous he had worked for a landscape gardener who also happened to be a friend of the family called Matt. Matt was a top bloke. He was single, self-employed, a devout Christian in his early fifties that owned his own small, local landscaping business. Both my brothers and I originally met him through a Christian-run youth group on our council estate when we were in our early teens. It was a church-funded programme to keep kids out of trouble and he was one of the volunteers.

An extremely busy man, Matt was always on the move. From working minimum ten-hour days to helping friends, family, youth groups, the church, drug addicts, neighbours with just about anything from moving houses to listening to their problems, he would help anybody and tried his best to help everybody. A real force of nature and a fantastic role model while I was growing up. We all stayed in contact with him after we left the youth group and left school. By the time we grew into young men, he'd become a friend to the whole family. Christmases, birthdays, any celebration or gathering he was there, he was a very positive part of all our lives, and we all appreciated his friendship deeply.

When he reached his late forties, he began to accept his impossible lifestyle and huge work demand could no longer be sustained by himself alone and took my older brother on as his first ever employee to lighten the load of the business a bit. But with my older brother heading off to the capital and looking to make a serious commitment to his girlfriend, Matt needed a replacement and wanted to take me on to fill my brother's role.

We met one evening in a little country pub in a village about ten miles outside the town to talk over the various points of my employment.

He explained that although he paid my brother ten pound an hour, he would only be offering me eight. This wasn't to tuck me up or take advantage, and I believed him. He hadn't calculated the wages properly, with sickness, holiday and pension input and was running at a slight loss when he took my brother on and he would be reluctant to increase the charges to his customers in order to compensate as he had already increased his rates only the year before. I would receive statutory sick pay and the minimum holiday allowance of twenty days per year, not including bank holidays. Work was Monday to Friday and would commence each morning at eight and we would aim to finish around five o'clock every day but the work came first and we couldn't leave until either the job at hand was finished, the property looked neat and tidy or a significant amount of work was achieved on any projects we were doing. I would get three breaks a day. Fifteen minutes in the morning, a forty-five-minute lunch and fifteen minutes in the afternoon.

It was a cut in pay, a cut in holiday and never any chance of advancement, but finally, I would be working for a good person whom I trusted and who wouldn't try to screw me over in some way or go back on his word. I accepted all of his terms and began straight after my brother finished working his notice.

It truly was an amazing job. Every day I worked somewhere different, I worked on something different and my surroundings never fell short of beautiful. I was taken all over the finer points of the county working in some of the most picturesque places you could imagine. Idyllic little villages that seemed to be owned mostly by the wealthy. That was Matt's entire clientele, there was no one on his business Christmas cards list that fell beneath a yearly six figure sum. Old money and new money alike, but they were all clever money too. They were never loud or brash or flashed the cash. They retreated into secluded country communities enjoying their wealth and luxurious living in almost total privacy. All the properties we worked on could stretch for miles. It could take us ten hours to cut the grass with a ride on lawn mower or for us to get to an area of work in the property we had to travel by quad bike with tools loaded in a trailer to cut down the time walking to and from a job. Hedge cutting could take weeks, not just a couple hours like the gardens I grew up around and to weed through all the flowerbeds on some properties could take up to a fortnight. They were all magnificent places.

Extravagant mansions, some, well over a hundred years old complete with swimming pools, tennis courts, rivers that ran throughout the property, vegetable gardens and mini-forests on the borders of the land where their families of dogs could run freely and safely all day. How the other half live indeed, but I will say that every one of the customers were lovely, charming people as well. Very friendly despite how much Matt charged them! We were never short of a cup of tea, a biscuit and some polite conversation while we worked through their grounds and Matt wouldn't have it any other way. You see, to Matt, manners came before the money. He wouldn't work for anybody who was rude or obnoxious. Over two years I witnessed him turn down dozens of potential customers because they were disrespectful or looked down their noses at others and I had a huge amount of respect for him for that.

I absolutely loved this job. It was outdoors, physical, simple and varied. I could spend all day strimming fields or mowing lawns in the summer, enjoying the sunshine without a care in the world. On the rainy days it was always weeding duties, which never bothered me at all. A lot of people would have been put off by standing in the pouring rain for hours on end getting soaked, cold and muddy, but I really didn't mind it. We had waterproof jackets and I had a set of sturdy headphones I could plug in and listen to stories or music all day while I worked.

My favourite work was the projects we took on because every job was unique through the challenges it presented. We built fences, new flower beds, walls, patios, drives, barbeques, tree houses, sheds, even zip lines for the customers' kids. With every job I picked up a new skill, a new little piece of knowledge I could only gain by getting stuck in and getting my hands dirty. I may have not been picking up qualifications, but my experience and general skill set were growing.

I made the small salary I earned stretch to cover the bills and food because I didn't want to be anywhere else. The splinters, blisters, skin slices, cuts and bruises from a good day's graft never fazed me either because I knew how lucky I was to be able to sit down and share my coffee flask with a friend at morning break and put the world to rights. I knew how fortunate I was to have a huge sense of freedom in my job knowing others were not so lucky and I never took it for granted. I also never looked too far into the future at that point, probably should have but I'd learned to enjoy each day in front of me for what it was. I felt peace and contentment that could only exist by working so close with nature and privacy. I was starting to believe I'd landed my perfect job and that I'd finally found a calling.

As much as Matt was a dear friend and a great boss, he did have his faults too. As a self-employed/small businessman, he was also one of the most unorganised people I'd ever met in my life and yet he genuinely believed he was one of the most organised people around at the same time. Why he thought this I would never know because it bordered on the delusional and it made watching him organise himself every day all the more frustrating knowing to advise or correct him on anything would be met with personal offence taken.

I was told to always be at his house at eight o'clock on the dot every day and ready to go. Not once in the entire time I worked for him was I ever late and was he ever ready? Each workday morning consisted of observing him at various stages of his morning routine. He could still be having breakfast, or he was upstairs brushing his teeth. Some mornings he wouldn't even be fully dressed as he flapped around his small, dated one-bed house performing a series of tasks simultaneously. Flicking the kettle on and trying to find his keys, workbook, boots and wallet while a charred bit of toast was hanging out of his mouth all at the same time. It was always chaotic, he was always stressed and flustered and that was before we even got to the tool thing! Oh, the bloody tools. Every morning we had to completely reload his work truck as he would always empty it out into his garage the night before and it was always a pain in the arse as his truck had one of those large, solid, plastic shells bolted to the rear. It was too low to stand up in and the floor was too hard to kneel down on as it was lined with thick corrugated black plastic, so I would spend the first half-hour of each morning hunched over in the back of a dirty vehicle, looking as though I was suffering from a severe back problem trying to load hand tools on. That wasn't a problem, though annoying as it was. The problem was he didn't let me load it by myself; he couldn't let that part of his routine go. He was so anal about how his tools were loaded I had to be supervised every time. The only part of the job I couldn't be left alone with was loading a spade and a fork on to a covered pickup truck as he was worried that I might forget something, which was something he did all the time. I wasn't allowed to help him get ready in the morning either, not even unlock the garage, drive the truck around to the tool area or

107

make his cup of coffee. I had to sit on his garden wall about three feet from his open, white plastic back door and watch my boss bumble about his home while I wondered, what the hell I had to turn up so early for. He would perform this daily routine of stress and chaos while at the same time telling me how disorganised I was because I may have forgotten something from my lunch pack that day.

We were lucky if we ever got to a customer before ten o'clock after the travel time, which was always awkward and embarrassing, particularly when most customers expected an earlier and more professional arrival.

I would stand back and observe in amazement as he seemed to stumble through his life both personally and professionally as he constantly let people down with punctuality whilst constantly telling me that I was warped in my decision making, constantly making bad life choices as a result.

The last six months of my employment with him were rather uncomfortable ones and it was because of a sudden change in his attitude towards me. Again, it wasn't that I was a bad employee. (I keep on declaring this, but it really is them, promise.) I very rarely took a day off with ill health. I was always on time. Always hard working and always tried to appear and act professionally. I was always polite with all the customers, and always stayed on later than I had to, to make sure projects that overran were finished as soon as possible, sometimes even without extra pay, letting an hour go here or there purely out of loyalty to him.

The change in his behaviour had come about because of a decision I made in my personal life. My girlfriend at that time had cheated on me. Not just a one-night-stand either, it was a full-blown affair lasting a couple of months and, worst of all, it was with one of my rugby club mates. He'd only been at the club less than a year and was new to the sport, but I'd also known this guy since I was at primary school. His mum was one of my schoolteachers, too. (Lovely lady.)

I used to go to his house after school a couple of evenings a week and play games together and sometimes stay for tea or he would come to mine and play and we did this right up until we were ten years old. Then he and his family moved away, out of town and to a new school. So, fifteen years later when my first ever bestest primary school pal had turned up out of nowhere to my spiritual home (the rugby club) wanting to learn the best game in the world, I was delighted and happy to see him back in the area and immediately took him under my wing. I helped him with the rules of the game, some training and the most important bit of any community rugby club, I did my utmost to get him involved in the social side and feel part of the family. What I didn't know during that time was he'd had his eyes on my girlfriend and she had hers on him and they began an affair.

When it all came out, I was heartbroken and mortified and it was all played out in public for everyone to see. The whole rugby club, dearest friends since I joined at thirteen years of age begged me to open my eyes and pay closer attention to their blatant and outrageous behaviour with each other whenever we went out. I tried to ignore it all, bury my head in the sand and pretend it wasn't happening, all the over-the-top flirting and the intense looks they gave one another, excuses she made to pop round and see him on her own. Their constant denial at any accusations put to them by concerned friends and myself at one point only fuelled my enduring ignorance.

Eventually the truth came out. They were seen together at his house by one of my friends when she said she was out on a work training course that evening and let's just say they weren't taking part in a "corporate strategy presentation" when they were caught. My friend came over immediately to tell me what he had witnessed, and I went straight over to his house to confront them both. He denied everything and lied repeatedly to my face but eventually my girlfriend came out of his house and come clean about the whole thing. I moved out of our shared house that night and moved back in with my mum.

I'd hit rock bottom emotionally. I'd been totally humiliated in front of everyone at my rugby club, my local pub and everybody I cared about, especially when word got out that the affair had been confirmed. Dozens of regulars and friends discussing my agony and embarrassment like it was hot gossip between each mouthful of their alcoholic beverages. I felt very low, very vulnerable and alone, especially when mutual friends began stepping back in an effort not to take sides over the unfolding drama. I never blamed them for doing that; they were in an impossible situation, but it was hard to watch.

After a few weeks of separation, she comes over to see me at my mum's one evening with her tail tucked firmly between her legs. My old and bestest primary school pal who had quite a reputation for being a bit of a man whore shocked absolutely no one when he binned off my ex after a very short time (days) once the thrill of the chase was over and there she was, standing in my mum's living room telling me what a huge mistake she had made and begging me to let her back in and give her another chance. That night I ignored every instinct, every doubt I had and made one of the most stupid decisions of my life. I agreed to give "us" another go. Why? Why did I do it? I'd always had such strict rules about this kind of thing. If you cheat, then you don't respect the person you're with. Love, or what you perceive to be love doesn't even have to enter it. When I look back on it now, I always ask myself: why? And what were you thinking? The only explanation I can offer you is that at the time she appeared genuinely remorseful and I was still very, very low mentally at the time, in the midst of grieving and I had crawled into a lonely world of isolation and anxiety because of what had happened and how it had happened. I still loved her at that time; that doesn't just disappear straight away even though she was the one who broke my heart. Her proposal was a way to ease some of the pain I was feeling and get back the person I was grieving for.

Despite all my personal problems followed by poor decisions I managed to get on with my job throughout with relative ease. It really didn't affect my work at all because it was like I could be a different person throughout the day, able to step out of my own life and examine it all from a distance while remaining focused on the job at hand, and it really helped me process everything. There was a real distance between work me and personal me up until Matt found out.

I explained earlier he was a good family friend, and it didn't take him long to get up to speed with everything from one of my brothers, and then he asked me what was going on during a lunch break.

I laid it all out to him over a cup of coffee and a sandwich in the cab of his red truck, but it wasn't sitting with him. From the moment my confession finished leaving my lips I saw a change in him instantly. His voice, his face, his body language all suddenly closed off from me. It just didn't chalk up to his unflinching moral code. I got the feeling that I had betrayed him in some way. I failed to live up to his high expectations as a moral being and all that was left was a clear and deep disappointment, and he wouldn't let it go either. From the day I told him, it had become a bit in his teeth he needed to work out of his mouth, and it went on for weeks. My workdays were then filled with constant questions about me, my personal life, my relationship and my choices, no matter how many times I tried to gently steer the conversation in another direction. His behaviour steadily worsened too. He started becoming hyper critical of every bit of work I did; my standards were the same as ever and good enough for the eighteen months before. As more time passed it grew into him making shitty comments about my appearance and professionalism that were again unchanged in the scope of his constant negative view of me. A resentment was building in him towards me and it was both sad and horrible to experience from someone I cared about.

A job that had brought so much happiness and fulfilment for eighteen months had very quickly turned into another occupation I dreaded the alarm clock going off for. I felt gutted, I saw a wonderful employment and a good friendship that I valued deeply slipping away in front of me. I tried to stick it out, staying focused on my work and out of his way as much as possible hoping some time would begin to heal some of the wounds that had opened up between us, but it was no good. The resentment began to turn into moments of full-blown anger. He would have fits and outbursts over the slightest error or tiniest mistakes. Launching chainsaws across the forest floor when I forgot to bring the fuel can from the truck, a dressing down if I left an inconsequential gate slightly ajar on the property or have a go at me for not bringing up a tool he needed, but didn't ask for, attacking a lack of common sense rather than realise I had no clue what he was doing because he never told me. I paid it all as little attention as possible but that only seemed to anger him further. When he wasn't getting the reaction he was looking for from his outbursts, he moved onto other areas; next up was the terms of my pay. The change was that I would no longer be paid at the time I arrived at his house; it would be from the time we arrived at the job. The way he saw it, he shouldn't have to pay me through a time I wasn't doing anything. Which was fair enough, of course, I shouldn't, except for the fact that he made me sit on his back wall for almost an hour each morning while he crashed through his house trying to sort his life out before I could begin loading the tools. There was no protest to the changes but now there was no pressure to get out the door in the morning, so Matt took even longer getting ready. So after a month of being kept waiting well over an hour each morning and not being paid to do it, I suggested that maybe he should start picking me up in the morning once he was ready and the tools were loaded as I was no longer being paid. He agreed reluctantly, but this pissed him off even more. He could no longer blame anyone else for his tardiness as it was all on his shoulders, which made him even angrier, but I still refused to react to his awful behaviour.

It took about five months after the affair, persistent ear bashings, rants and put downs for the line to finally be crossed to a place where his behaviour had become unacceptable.

We were weeding one morning at one of our regulars in a village just outside Salisbury, working closely together and sifting through the same flower beds on a very wet and horrible day. The morning had been a typical one since his "change of view". Total silence in the truck en route, minimal talking on arrival only to dish out his instructions for the day, then we got to work. After about half an hour and plenty of time to think about the conversation in his head he finally engaged me with more personal questioning. He began asking about my girlfriend's new job. I explained she had started at a bank sorting out PPI claims and she seemed pleased with her new role, she was happy about the increased salary, better working hours and all the perks that came with it. The conversation continued and with each question, and every answer I gave him, he became more and more angry and frustrated and as it carried on, he began making horrible little comments after each answer I offered.

He asked me if she worked in a big team at her new place to which I replied "yes, I think so", then he immediately muttered straight away after: "Probably loads of men in that team, flirting with her, eyeing her up, bet she's loving it. Does she speak to customers over the phone?"

"Yes, I believe so."

"Probably trying it on with them too."

It was becoming nasty, indirect aggression and really peculiar behaviour. Anyone would think he was the one who'd been cheated on. I wasn't ramming my life down his throat; he was seeking this information out, then getting wound up over it. It was really strange.

The questions continued to come, and I continued to answer as calmly and politely as possible. I did my utmost to dismiss the horrible little comments that were following each answer until eventually he snapped.

He stood upright from the weeding, drove his gardening fork down into the wet mud of the weeding bed with all the strength he had, looked me dead in the eye and said loudly and clearly:

"Your girlfriend is a fucking cheating whore!"

"HEY! You're being right out of order now, Matt. You've got no right to talk to me like that and you've got no right to talk about my girlfriend like that, no fucking right whatsoever, do you understand me! It's fuck all to do with you, so back off!"

By now the customer Annie had come to her living room window to see why she could hear raised voices. Matt and I were just standing there looking at each other. Adrenaline clearly flowing through both of us. Our eyes stayed locked for no more than a few seconds, but it seemed like an eternity until eventually Matt had begun to calm down. He muttered something else, but I couldn't make it out as he had begun to turn away. He retrieved his gardening fork from the bed and walked away. He spent the rest of the day working right over on the other side of the property.

We didn't speak for the rest of the day until we were at the back of the truck, packing the tools up at around five o'clock. I sat and had my lunch alone in the garden that day while he sat in the truck. He approached me and apologised begrudgingly about his outburst. Acknowledging the gesture and choosing to ignore the lack of effort he put into it I also apologised for losing my temper and with that I tried to build a small bridge back by saying I understood that he was coming from a place of concern. I thought at the time maybe that set-to was needed for us to clear the air on the issue and move forward (even though it was my business). I hoped that would be the end of it all and I could get my friend back. We finished loading up the truck and headed home to put an end to the working week and leave the day behind us.

Monday morning, tools unpacked, back at Annie's to tackle the shrubs and hedges. This time I'm pruning. We're about an hour in and Matt gingerly approaches where I'm working. I could tell something was going on because his walk was completely off. He'd replaced his normal, confident wide-legged, slightly cowboy looking strut to a shy neighbour creeping around in an awkward shell to talk to you about the damaged middle fence they believe is your responsibility and dropping the major hint they want it fixed. "Can I have a word?" he asked over-politely.

"Sure, Matt, what's up?"

"I've had a good, long think over the weekend about things and I've decided that it's just not working out you being here, and I think maybe it's time that you moved on and found somewhere else to work."

"Okay, erm, I don't really know what to say."

"Look, you're a good worker but I don't think your heart's really in this job, to be honest, and it needs to be if we're always going to deliver a good standard and also things have become a bit stale in our working relationship in the last few months and it's not a good environment to work in and at the end of the day it is my business and I need to be comfortable with the guy I'm working with."

"I see, fair enough, that's honest, okay, no worries, Matt, I'll begin looking for work. I'm just really sorry it's come to this."

He completely dismissed my apology and instead focused on the speech he had rehearsed and locked in his head. "If you could sort of work a month's notice, I think it's fair as you will leave with basically a full month's pay and I can begin finding a more suitable replacement."

He was trying his best to sound professional and reasonable in an effort to save face. I thought he came across as an insulting, snivelling prat, full of pride. "Yes, of course, no worries," I replied, and he walked back to where he was working.

I stayed where I was and continued to prune. I gradually moved around the back of the large shrub until I was out of his sight before I shed my first tears. People always say never work for family or friends. I always thought it was because liberties could be taken from one side of the relationship or conflict could arise from taking an almost equal relationship and putting it into a hierarchy and watching the dynamics change. I thought I'd anticipated every potential problem when I agreed to work for him, by accepting he was my boss in work, but I learned from this experience that friendships can break down from areas you can't prepare for because you never knew they existed in the first place. One poor choice in my personal life, in my relationship, had ended up costing me my job and my friend further down the road. How could I ever see that coming?

Once the notice had been "agreed" the heavy atmosphere seemed to lift a little for both of us, relief for him that I was going, relief for me because his verbal destruction had completely ceased.

The saddest part in all of it is that he still has great relationships and frequent contact with both my brothers and I've only seen him twice in the last six years since I left his business. One being at my grandfather's funeral where he acknowledged and apologised for his behaviour for those six months a lot more sincerely than the first time. He admitted to

117

really overstepping the mark and that it was completely out of character. I accepted it again and we buried any and all ill feelings that day, but we wouldn't be friends again. Our relationship had been too badly damaged while working together and would never be like it was before.

As for work? I was offered a job opportunity during my notice, funnily enough, from one of Matt's old customers, to go and work for her full time, which I will tell you about next. And my girlfriend? Turns out she'd been sleeping with a male colleague on her PPI team. I found out a couple of months into my new employment and that it had been going for a while. She denied it all, of course, exactly as she did at the beginning of the first affair, desperately trying to swallow her own bullshit as well as feed it to me at the same time, a lying little jellyfish that couldn't do the decent thing second time around and come clean. My cousin worked in the same building and saw them together. He got pictures of them snogging and leaving the office late together holding hands. She never boxed clever when she was with other men; only this time she couldn't explain any of it away once I'd shown her the photos I'd been sent. Knowing she'd been exposed as an out and out liar, she turned angry and cold towards me straight away as though I was the one in the wrong. She was more concerned about being proved as a cheat rather than the hurt she caused me a second time. True colours shown. I found out how little she really cared about me. I moved out of the flat within two days of the discovery and into my friend's place as he had a room up for rent.

Two years after doing the dirty on me again I found out she was also being played by the guy she was having an affair with. All that time she was fucking me over she was being two-timed by a colder reptile than herself. He was seeing my ex on a Monday to Friday basis in Hampshire, then on weekends he would return to Reading, telling her it was to be with his kids. He was actually trying to play happy families with his cancer-ridden wife. That poor, poor, woman, his wife obviously, not my ex! Last I heard she pulled through the cancer and slung him out. (I digress, but I thought you'd like to know.) I felt nothing second time around, I got the measure of her in the end and realising that's just who she was made the infidelities very easy to deal with.

A very successful businesswoman by the name of Charlotte became my next employer. A strikingly beautiful, fit and energetic yoga queen in her fifties. Thanks to the help of an expensive personal trainer every morning and the benefits of a wealthy lifestyle no doubt contributed to her looking extraordinarily young for a woman of her age. She had the poshest accent I'd ever encountered too. We knew each other from my previous employment with Matt where we worked on her property one day a week, so there was no awkward introduction or interview. She approached me about the position. Charlotte had heard through the grapevine that I was working my notice with Matt and got my contact details through her stable lady and offered me the job. I was flattered by the effort, to be honest; she was a very busy and powerful woman in her world and had taken the time to reach me personally. I automatically felt valued by her efforts. The job was three days a week. Three breaks a day including a full hour for lunch and I would be on a hundred pound a day. All hand, digging and power tools would be supplied by her for the work. It was an amazing offer. I couldn't refuse it or even try to negotiate it.

I had been given the chance to carry on in a job I really enjoyed and at the same time work for a very pleasant family.

The property was incredible. A six-bedroom three-storey old manor house at least a hundred years old. Inside it was clean and fresh, a very modern feel to it with expensive, up to the minute furnishings with old portraits, paintings and antiques blending in perfectly to add a classy and elegant feel to their grand home. Three living rooms, a dining suite, an open plan kitchen, a wine cellar and a giant curving stairwell that dominated the front of the house as you entered. The front lawn was a neat and well-designed rose garden that was situated in beds dug into the lawn itself, and the front of the house had a four-foot wide, stone-edged, wild flower bed running all the way across it. And from the back of these wild flower beds were more white roses and they had to be decades old as they ran all the way up the front walls of the house, manipulated around all the windows and stone carvings and climbed up as high as the third floor of the house. They had been well maintained through the years and affixed to the house with wiring, netting and small hooks. You could see more rose than wall and, in the spring, when they bloomed it was a stunning sight. I'd seen many attempts at this effect over the years but I'd never seen one come off quite so beautifully.

The view of the house wasn't there to be enjoyed by everyone, though. Only guests or visitors who were invited into the property. Their home was right on the edge of a main country road that ran through the whole village, so to ensure privacy they grew a very tall and very neat conifer hedge twelve feet high concealing its beauty from the neighbours and anybody passing through. The remainder of the property was screened off by a ten-foot brick wall, almost as old as the house and an electric, tall, white wooden gate as the only other access. Inside they had their own vegetable garden, stables in which all the walls were covered with more white roses, two horse paddocks, a one-bedroom cottage on the grounds, a tennis court, a back lawn the size of two football pitches, a miniature forest and dozens of flower beds filled with hundreds of different types of beautiful and exotic specimens that it could take a solid week to weed through it all.

Out of all of Matt's customers, Charlotte's was my favourite place to work, so I was very happy to be able to go back there.

My duties would be exactly the same as before. All the garden maintenance I did before, but I would be there three days a week instead of one, so I was also to be an odd job/handyman/caretaker type guy too. This basically meant anything that needed doing around the whole property including within the home was my responsibility. Repairing fences, tree cutting, grass cutting, log splitting, weeding, painting internally and externally, building or moving furniture, shopping, dump/tip runs, fixing toilets, repairing roofs, the occasional school runs, driver to and from some of their social engagements, house sitting and any DIY jobs that didn't involve structural alterations fell within my remit. I covered basically everything from putting up shelves to repairing the dishwasher or maintaining the tennis courts, I turned my hand to anything.

The whole property always had to look on point at all times as they constantly received and entertained very rich and important guests at the very top of our social ladder. Business lunches, formal dinners and garden parties for CEOs, celebrities and sports icons alike, all to secure contracts for her husband's gambling company.

Their business was all about how they sold their product; hosting and impressions were their skill set, so the place couldn't look anything less than perfect.

I worked very hard every day I was there, always trying to learn something new, getting to know the property like the back of my hand. On the days I didn't work for the family I was always trying to pick up some extra work here and there, top up my wages and get some new customers. In fact, Charlotte, impressed by my work ethic, began recommending me to some of her friends and after a few months, my whole week was filled with regular work and I was earning very good money from it.

I was starting to buy my own tools, save a little each month and live comfortably. Life felt stress free and I felt I was in a job where my efforts were always appreciated.

Just over a year into the job and Charlotte had decided a fresh pair of hands would be needed on her property to "move the gardens in a different direction", as she put it, and my services would no longer be required.

I found out later through another landscape gardener that worked in the same village that I had been undercut massively for the job.

The young guy who would be replacing me agreed to take on my three days a week for almost the minimum hourly rate. How was he able to do this? Rent in the area was one of the highest in the country and the cost of living seemed to be constantly rising. How could he sell himself so short in what could be a very physically demanding job at times?

Answer, he had free accommodation on another rich family's land in a little cottage for him and his partner. They got a free meal every day too. In return, all he had to do was perform fifteen hours of maintenance and gardening on their property as payment. This meant his biggest expenditures were covered and he could go out, look for more work and charge whatever he liked in order to secure the job. I just couldn't afford to compete with those rates; not many could. Situations like mine were beginning to creep up in and around the local area and it was pissing a lot of tradesmen off because these new, low rates being offered everywhere were untouchable and work was being eaten up in cheap, half-paid labour.

I wasn't angry, though, I didn't feel cheated or hard done by over the situation. The truth is I actually felt quite grateful to Charlotte for giving me the chance to continue something I loved for another year, especially at a time when I felt that door had started to close on me. I wasn't ready to give up gardening after Matt and Charlotte helped me hold onto it for a little longer.

As employers Charlotte and her family were always polite, friendly, sweet and accommodating people and I loved being part of their set up. How could I be bitter about going after what she had given me? In their world, money talks and money dictates, that's just the way it is. They don't retain their wealth through sentiment or careless spending; it's retained through good business and sensible decisions. I understood it was nothing personal. She did it to Matt, the guy before Matt and she was going to do it to the poor sod who undercut himself eventually.

Charlotte gave me a month's notice, which I fulfilled, and I left on good terms with her.

Although I loved the solitude and tranquillity that gardening offered, I was approaching my late twenties and I felt the time was right for me to land a more secure job in an environment with structure and a possibility of some advancement in the future. So I began looking and applying once more, and I also signed with a new agency in town that had only been up and running a few weeks in the hope they weren't loaded up with small temp jobs that they needed me to do first and luckily enough they weren't — something did come up which I will explain in the next chapter. As for "Johnny undercut", whom Charlotte employed in my stead, he didn't start until after I left (so there was no handover). After just one week he had completely destroyed large parts of her flowerbeds through ill practice, severing roots while weeding and killing off very expensive and well-established plant life and he had caused considerable damage to her pricey ride-on lawnmower before he walked off the job never to return, leaving Charlotte without a gardener and trying to find another worker quickly. She was trying to contact me once more in desperation and as tempting as it was, I knew there was no future in it, I'd have been let go at the next opportunity, so I didn't answer the call.

# Chapter Six
## Who they were

I signed onto the new agency and within a week of being unemployed they found me a temp to perm contract. It was to go and work on a production line for a large and well-known mobility aids company in the heart of the town's industrial centre. No odd jobs, no months of bullshit this time, just straight into the contract. I did in all honesty give the opportunity a little nudge myself. I knew one of the line leaders at the factory. He was an old school friend called Steve (a different school friend from the guy sleeping with my girlfriend!) and he gave me a heads up of a job going at his place. I had to apply through the agency like everybody else — that was the company policy — but he would phone up and request me by name to get me in, which sure enough he did, and I started the following Monday, returning once more to the town's industrial estates which by that time seemed a lifetime apart from when I first went. I must admit I did feel a lot of guilt being able to pull some strings, I hated the whole "it's who you know world" we've created for ourselves, but it's impossible to avoid. I've always felt that people should make it on their own efforts and by merit. By this point, though, I was tired of being kicked around and left to swirl in uncertainty by the failure of others to keep their word and it was the one and only time in my working life I did pull in a favour to get some steady work. It was never an attitude of if you can't beat them join them; I was just fed up of being honest, putting in the effort and doing the right things and getting nowhere with it. I just wanted to work for someone who appreciated hard graft and if Steve could give me that opportunity, I was confident I could do the rest of it on my own.

Now before I move on, I'm going to change the format up a bit, because there is simply too much to divulge in this section and it requires a slightly different approach from the last few chapters.

So I'm going to tell you first of all, who they were, the people who made my working life and the working lives of others an absolute misery and then I'm going to tell you what they did, so I can cover as much as possible and not leave anything out.

I shall start from the bottom of this structure and work my way up.

## Line leaders

They were leaders in name only, they were former operators that were taken from the production lines, given a different coloured polo shirt and after tax made about an extra twenty quid a week and were told they were in charge of the lines they once worked on as well as the operators' health, wellbeing and also the results that came from those production lines. Now most people would look at that position as slightly senior to the operators but given the poor wage increase and the fact they couldn't wield any real authority or power they were no better than school prefects who tried their best to police students in the school hallways. They just grassed people up to their superiors who were able to deal with any potential issues; that was the full extent of their abilities. But to anyone who got the new coloured polo shirt they thought it made them God himself. It was pathetic; only small-minded and petty people filled those shirts.

They never inspired, they never motivated others, they never set a good example, gave praise, raised people's spirits, took an interest in the development of others or behaved in a way that could ever be described as positive or effective, they lacked the desire or the ability to do any of it. They were named leaders but showed nothing resembling leadership. These self-important simpletons put on an unstable and rocky pedestal had one single purpose, to carry out Rochelle's, the department manager's instructions. No matter how unfair, how unjust, how brutal or even illegal at times. They were to follow her orders or pack up their lockers and go, they weren't decent people and most of them historically weren't even good operators, they were well-trained dogs for her and picked because of their inability to act as free-thinking humans, they followed orders, enjoyed the status and at times seemed to enjoy the misery those orders brought about.

## Barry

I've already mentioned this slimy and wretched toad at the very beginning of this book. The smug, reptilian-looking bore fest inside a skinny, weedy, lactose-intolerant shell who looked as though a good workout or anything strenuous to build him up had passed him by. The type of bloke slowly growing depressed and regretful by the decision he made to make a family so young. Pretends he's happy each morning with his fibre-loaded, miniscule ration pack for break, loathingly shoved in his work bag by his depressed stay at home wife who lost respect for him years ago from discovering the spineless cretin he was. Hell of a jump, you may ask, why would I assume that? Because he was a sleaze that hit on young girls as soon as he got something that resembled authority and she knew all about it. I'll get more onto that later.

I'd see him every day, pouring his lactose-free nut extract milk into the same pathetic looking plastic tub with barely anything in it, trying his best to hide the disappointment that was desperately clinging to his face as he wished just once he could be given his spine to ask for a couple of quid back from his own wages from the Mrs to go and get himself a bacon sandwich instead of the Victorian prison offal, he had to face every day.

He'd been promoted about two months before I arrived and he felt as though he had to make an impact in the role straight away, to show he was as capable as the other two well-established line leaders. So how did he go about making this impression? Zero tolerance, to anything. Naming, shaming and grassing up colleagues and others in his team to Rochelle or the supervisors at every opportunity to demonstrate he was in authority and show she had made the right choice in promoting him. Example, two operators in the line who went above and beyond to help get a shipment of products out of the door. They found parts from other departments to complete the build, stayed on past their paid hours for an extra twenty minutes and really grafted to make life easier for the company, Barry and Rochelle by completing the order. When it was finished, they hinted at him about maybe putting them forward for a free breakfast at the work canteen (one of the last perks left, worth about a pound per head) for their efforts. Rather than confront the operators on the subject of dropping hints which was deserved and not really an issue, he smiled, laughed along at the tongue in cheek request and went straight up to tell Rochelle about how these two operators had put pressure on him in performing his role and demanding a reward. I shit you not! I knew the operators; they were never seriously chasing a one-pound incentive. Instead, he deliberately took it from its context and turned it into something petty and pathetic to show he wouldn't tolerate their behaviour. What made it even more tragic is Rochelle actually gave it credence and pulled these operators into a meeting and grilled them over their poor attitude. I couldn't believe it when I found out. A level of pettiness so low to engage would automatically drag you into a world beyond respect and reason.

With Barry and his dictatorship, you couldn't put a toe out of line. If you were five seconds late back from break? Five seconds! Seriously! Good luck in the office keeping your cool while he patronised you over being punctual knowing he was always frequently later than everyone else and wondering how the whole process was productive in the first place as the meeting took fifteen minutes over five seconds on one occasion. And if he really didn't like you or he was asked to target you specifically by Rochelle or the supervisors, he would pull into the office over things you didn't do to try and bully and intimidate you and make your life miserable knowing there was nothing you could do about it, nowhere you could turn until you either quit, were sacked or were worn down mentally and became compliant to their strict and harsh demands. He was a very sad piece of work but put in a place where he could cause damage to people who hated confrontation or lacked confidence and could make life pretty uncomfortable to anyone in his charge.

## Steve

Ah, my old mate Steve. I thought by putting my name forward for the job he was doing an old friend a favour. It turned out I was the one doing him the favour. I was there to make him look good; that was all. Once I was in, he didn't even want to associate with me. We had worked together at the parcel company years before. He knew I was a grafter, I was consistent, hardworking and I was there purely for him to feed off what I achieved, taking all of the credit for my work and efforts and anyone else who worked well for him. In the years we'd been out of touch he'd become a spineless blood sucker with vampire teeth.

The dear, sweet, young boy I grew up with and kicked a ball around with on our estate when we were little had turned into a gutless maggot who cared about only one thing, saving his own skin at whatever cost to anyone else. There was nothing about his character that earned the title of leader either because he only possessed two skills. Taking credit for other people's accomplishments or ideas and offloading his mistakes and failures onto other people. Even when confronted with the truth he would lie and lie and lie until you give up fighting your corner about him stealing your ideas. He didn't do it because he was a ruthless guy who was hungry for success, he did it because he was so insecure that he felt that was the only way to ensure his own survival in that position. I could have easily felt sorry for him, being so plagued by doubt, but I had none because his anxieties crossed a line into affecting other people through dishonesty and deception, so to me, taking that job and behaving the way he did made him just as bad as the rest of them.

If anyone came forward to Steve with an idea of how to speed up or improve production, he would immediately go and tell Rochelle he had come up with the idea. It was such slimy behaviour. He had been devoid of confidence as a young boy and it had manifested itself into a shallow, self-interested figure who worried only about retaining a status (which was only a fucking line leader in a factory, not a top government position!) and lacked the capability to shoulder an ounce of the responsibility he was supposed to.

He was a tall and a slightly plump young man. Mid-twenties and going bald, fast. He had a tick in which he would constantly pull his shirt away from his body as if he felt it was clinging too much to his nipple line and mid-section and if the fabric stayed there too long it would quickly reveal how much he was perspiring underneath the leader's top. He was very body conscious and insisted on wearing baggy tops at least two sizes too big and he was also a complete fucking dimwit who genuinely believed his status meant he automatically had more life experience and intelligence than those in his charge. He could have also been the national champion of shit, last word arguments too. No matter how idiotic or undignified he came across he had to have the last word before walking away every time because in his little brain that was a win, his authority had been stamped through a last utterance and it was awkward to witness this child-like behaviour displayed by a fully grown man responsible for others.

If he asked you to do something and it was wrong, that wouldn't matter either; it would always be someone else's fault. In the four years that I worked with him he never ever made a single mistake, not once was anything his fault, incredible that, a guy that perfect should have been a lot higher than the warehouse grasser.

I began referring to him as an old friend very quickly after starting at the company because I couldn't be friends with someone like that, I disassociated myself from him. Our friendship belonged in the past with the good memories I kept of him. I didn't recognise him any longer. He had become a selfish, arrogant, empty but programmable vessel ready to carry out any instructions given to him without ever questioning the impact of those instructions on other people and as long as he was okay and maintained a position slightly off from the bottom then he was happy.

## Mathew

A vile human being and truly one of the worst people I've ever met in my life. Physically he was a wreck. Morbidly obese with the majority of all his fat stored around his hips, thighs and belly. A gut so fat and flabby it hung a good three inches over his trousers line all the way around his body preventing you from seeing any of his belt if he actually owned one or half of his zipper. His appearance was made to look a lot more animated by the fact he also owned the skinniest arms, chest and shoulders. It was as if someone tried to build a scarecrow out of water balloons, and when it was propped up, all the water was pulled down towards the earth leaving something that barely resembled the shape of a human being. I know, I know, how horrible it is to describe someone in such a foul way, body shaming somebody, who do I think I am? Nobody is perfect! You're right. Entering my mid-thirties and not exactly taking care of myself I'm definitely starting to resemble something close to a melted candlestick too close to a fireplace. I highlight his body because he did, he made his obesity project onto others and how he treated them. His body was a result of his living, not his vulnerabilities, and the fact that he constantly ripped others apart and degraded them over their appearance knowing there was no reprisals because of his position made me think this total hypocrite was fair game. He was about thirty-four when I started, and he had lived at home with his mum all his life with no attempts to move out. Now this isn't shameful in itself, actually quite common given the financial difficulties a lot of us are facing these days (I still don't have my own home either!), but the difference is not once did he ever pay his way. He never contributed a single penny towards his single mother's household or bills or even treated his mother to a present, a meal or a shopping trip as a way of saying thank you for his rent and carefree living; she was even paying for his holidays abroad. He was a thirty-four-year-old spoiled brat who barely knew beyond wiping his own pale white arse. How do I know? Because he constantly bragged about it all like they were accomplishments, something to be proud of. He would also add things into the conversations like "and I get half that house when she's gone" or "why am I bothered, she earns enough money to keep me there", he had absolutely no love, no feelings, no compassion or sympathy, even towards his own mother.

He'd spent all of his twenties high on crack and coke and any other drug he could get his hands on, rotting his teeth to the point it looked as though somebody was constantly shitting in his mouth, damaging his body with an unflinching diet of alcohol and fast food. He learned nothing of consequence or living for something beyond his own experiences, selfish to the very core.

When he hit his thirties, he got his big promotion (well, I say big promotion, it was once more the rural warehouse line leader's position). He eased off the class A's (not completely) and used his money to rent himself an executive car. Still not a penny to his mum or an attempt to save up and buy a vehicle of his own, because he'd miss out continuing to shove the white powdered crap up his nose. He rented a car one of our directors would drive about six spots above him in the company, a position he lacked the grace or intelligence to ever reach.

Now you may think I'm being very harsh and may suggest all his behaviours stem from deep, deep insecurities about his weight, appearance, addictions, lifestyle and an inability to form deep and meaningful relationships with people as a result, maybe. For me all I ever saw was a selfish, heartless and cruel prick and ultimately isn't it all about how you treat other people? He made a conscious choice to treat employees, some vulnerable in ways with discontent every day and as far as I'm concerned, he deserves all the criticism he gets for making people's lives miserable.

The only emotion I ever saw him display was joy at other people's misery. He would shout and scream and bully young girls who rejected his grotesque advances, on the spot, in front of everyone and then laugh when they began to cry or walk away upset. He showed pure delight every time he caused upset, the more emotion from his victims the better. Soulless, a massive brown nose and the biggest hypocrite going too. Briefing out repeatedly about the company's zero tolerance towards drug use and reminding everyone about the "random" testing that could take place, which wasn't random at all. It was done on the line leader's request, which meant he could continue snorting his life away knowing he would never be checked or tested for it. He was the perfect model for Rochelle's blueprint.

## Supervisors

The next notch up from line leaders. They were officially called area line leaders and they thought of themselves as junior management, but they were nothing more than supervisors. They had no real power; they couldn't act on a single thing without Rochelle's say so either. Instead of wearing a different coloured polo shirt like the line leaders they got to wear a white, uniformed shirt and black work issue trousers, but despite still wearing a uniform it didn't stop them from thinking they were something different and special, walking around like they were some sort of office big shots from the city because they no longer dressed like the factory workers. I never really saw the point in their position, to be honest, other than being something slightly more senior than the prefects beneath them. If someone had to be disciplined or punished, it was their responsibility, but they had to go to Rochelle for permission to do so. They detached themselves from production totally despite the fact they were supposed to be in charge of production and the operators, always finding new little projects that pulled them away from their jobs and gave them the opportunity to avoid their duties while demonstrating what assets they were to the company in other areas like monitoring locker usage or how many times the coffee machine was used in a day, real important, vital and revolutionary stuff! Their primary function was to be the voice and face of Rochelle as she was far too busy and important to interact with her own staff but they were too introverted to speak to us as well as feed all our concerns and suggestions to Rochelle, which they never did because they didn't care about their staff and took no interest in what we had to say. The only time they spoke to their teams was when they absolutely had to. Disciplinaries, absence meetings or company briefings. Beyond that there was nothing, no rapport or communication or attempt to get to know the people who worked under them. They were minimalist in their approach to inspire or lead because it would mean rising beyond the box ticking of leadership and they weren't prepared to do it, too much like hard work.

## Colin

This will be the only time I will mention Colin in this book, why? Because he was a boring human being and didn't do much. He had come straight off a production line himself that produced modern mid-range managers that lacked any sort of personality at all. From the immaculate haircut down to the pristine shoes and company issued shirt. Equipped to deal with any situation with managerial clichés, calming solutions and problem-solving techniques straight out of the managers' "how to" manual, unchanged, word for word from the procedures he absorbed from its pages always in a calm, quiet and forgetful tone.

In his mid-thirties straight out from college (late starter) with qualifications in production and quality control. Being more qualified for the job on paper than her, Rochelle snapped him up from outside the business and offered him a supervisor's position.

The reason I note him here is not because he was an intentionally horrible person like the rest of them, it's because of what he didn't do. He wasn't at all like the others, he didn't take class As, he didn't bully or threaten people or sack them for made up reasons, he didn't even raise his voice, but he also said nothing to the people who did.

The only characteristic that stood out of the very boring man was greed and ambition made apparent by his blind eye and inaction. You knew to look at him that what he witnessed every day felt wrong to him, but to go against their behaviour would be to go against Rochelle herself and that was his ticket out of that position and up the ladder. The supervisor's role for him was merely a stepping-stone; with his qualifications he wanted the job heading up quality. Head of quality was about three times the salary and a higher position than Rochelle's within the business and it was promised to him by Rochelle when the head of quality at that time retired (which wasn't far off), and he wasn't going to do anything to jeopardise it.

His failure to act on the things he saw made him as culpable as the rest of his leadership team, chasing all the opportunities while turning his back on all the staff in his care that were being bullied or ill-treated. We can also add nepotism to his list too. He landed the head of quality job about two years after joining and the sweetheart he hooked up with from his production line somehow managed and no one knows how, to land the PA to the quality head job despite having none of the qualifications, no interview and the job never being advertised. They didn't even bother with the charade of a faked interview process. Instead, they just rubbed the corruption in all of our faces knowing the issues would never be raised above their level; between them all and with the help of HR they had a total monopoly on who got what opportunities in the business without it ever being checked or questioned. Colin's girlfriend was the laziest fucker in the place too, making the whole promotion thing even more frustrating. She did absolutely sod all in the factory but bang the right bloke at the right time; she then got to wear suits and office wear and we had to watch her come in every day and lord it over all the people she slacked off in front of like she was something special, forgetting she was the biggest work avoider going.

## Jimmy

A lot of girls at work regarded him as a good-looking guy. I really couldn't see it myself. No jealousy at all, I can't be bothered with all that bitterness, I'm confident enough in myself to admit when another guy is better looking, but with Jimmy I just couldn't work out what the attraction was.

He was over six-foot tall, he had very skinny legs like toothpicks and he looked underfed. I saw him in jeggings once (that's jeans so tight they look like leggings!) when he came into work on his day off to see Rochelle, attempting to look younger than he actually was and instead he just looked silly and malnourished.

He had ginger hair which he constantly dyed jet black even though everybody knew it was ginger. In his early thirties he possessed a baby face, definitely had a skin routine, he also had a lightly freckled face and dark, squinty brown eyes as if he'd spent his entire childhood sucking on a very bitter lemon.

Out of all the so-called supervisors, I felt he was the worst because he never cared one way or the other. He had no soul, no empathy. There was nothing there behind his small brown eyes. Rochelle had promoted him from line leader to supervisor not long after she was appointed as the department manager.

As a line leader I heard he was quite easy going. As long as you got the job done, he didn't care. He had a laugh with his team and held a good rapport with them, three guys in particular. He partied with them, stayed at their homes, went on hiking weekends with them and even small holidays. The four of them had a very tight bond that nobody minded or begrudged because they all knew it had been formed well before Jimmy became a line leader. In fact, it was a huge help because they could keep him grounded in his decision making and the way he treated other people, but as soon as he was given the white company shirt to trade for the red polo he completely changed his attitude towards everybody he worked with.

He also had a drug problem. Weed, ketamine, coke when he partied and although I never condoned it and never will, he kept it away from work and he never tried to sack or test others for their abuse. What did bother me was that he had a long-term girlfriend and a son he should have been taking care of instead; he was taking them for granted while he got high.

At work and before his second promotion Jimmy appeared to be a fun and approachable guy who never took himself too seriously. I think it all stemmed from his young adult years.

He was charged with arson in his late teens and did some time in young offenders as a result. What he actually did I'm not entirely sure; some say he torched a house but whatever it was, it was serious enough to warrant time in prison. Being troubled, off his face on all kinds of drugs and a reputation that preceded him as a loose cannon when he was younger, removed any kind of ambitions he may have had for professional success. He served his time and tried going honest and anyone who does that deserves a second chance, but in his head, he must have thought it was always going to hold him back with regard to promotion and climbing the ladder in the workplace, so he let it all go and became content with the role he had.

When Rochelle came in, she immediately had a soft spot for him and found him very easy on the eye. It was all helped along by Jimmy flirting outrageously with her in front of everybody, always way over the top and very embarrassing, so I was told. When he saw the flirting was having a considerable effect, he did more and more. Then he began to change. He started distancing himself from his friends, the ones keeping him out of arm's reach of the drugs, and also closing off from the rest of his team. He no longer cared for their time or their company, and even became dismissive and reserved when colleagues tried to approach him as he thought this professional distance gained favour with his new boss.

After a couple of months Rochelle promoted him up to supervisor level and the change was complete, the rest of it almost happening overnight. He'd been given another opportunity of making something of himself and he was going to hold onto it with both hands, no matter where it took him morally.

As soon as that white shirt was put on, he never approached his old team again, treating them as though they were total strangers in the way he talked, the way he spoke to them begrudgingly. As far as he was concerned, they were beneath him at that point and he had to constantly show that gap to Rochelle and everybody else in order to demonstrate he was someone in authority. Every day, he would go from his own, crummy little half-office, half-stationery cupboard up to Rochelle's place and back again, avoiding anybody below his position unless he absolutely had to engage with them. Another leader who never motivated, he didn't know what it was, he never spoke positively or gave praise — none of that existed in his repertoire — he wasn't interested in people or their development at all. The only time he showed any interest was if you were ill or having a really bad time at home. Then you were given a small amount of attention in making you feel bad or guilty for letting it affect your work in some way and if you didn't feel guilty, you were then pushed towards the door with intimidation of performance reviews and contract terminations.

After a few months, he did exactly the same as Mathew and what so many other fucknuts do when they get the tiniest of promotions, they seem to adopt delusions of grandeur and he got the car he thought matched his new status but in actual fact got a cash sucker well beyond his pay grade. Why on earth do you do that, boys and girls, why? Why do get the world's smallest promotion and tiniest pay rise by only a couple of quid, then go out and get a car that you can't afford and everybody knows you can't afford because you're only getting an extra twenty quid after tax and struggle with a ridiculously expensive motor? You're not kidding a soul! You think you look professional, successful and powerful, but I promise you, I promise you this, everybody else around you, thinks you're a debt-ridden bell end, we all know it's fake, trying to look like something you're not with your expensive-looking rent a car and we also think you're a joke. I'd say don't waste your time or money but even if someone came up and slapped you in the face with this information, I think you'd still ignore it.

As for Jimmy's friends, not only did he cut them completely, to go and roll in management circles, which always looked awkward, embarrassing and cringy watching him trying to bond with other snakes in the pit, but he also got rid of all his old chums from the company. The three guys he had close friendships with for over ten years, who were upset by his overnight attitude change, were seen as problems in Rochelle's eyes. To her they were part of the old guard and knew too much dirt on her favourite boy, so one by one she got rid of them. And she made Jimmy do it too, to test his loyalty; he did it, of course, without any flinching or hesitation. None of it was through legitimate means either. Accusations of racism, repeatedly lying about them breaking company policy like the use of mobile phones or eating on the production lines that could never be proved but were used to stain his old friends' records. They were all on Jimmy's word against theirs with the odd line leader stepping up to be a witness to an incident that never occurred. It was enough mud to stick on his old friends to fall into a disciplinary knowing they had neither the means, intelligence nor motivation to fight in a court or tribunal all for a seventeen grand a year job that they no longer enjoyed and didn't want to be in anyway.

Jimmy was thick as shit, but he was heartless, and that was exactly the type of guy Rochelle was looking for to control her staff. When Jimmy got promoted, he ditched his long-term girlfriend because her face no longer fit his changing lifestyle and got with a girl from the purchasing department who was just as big a self-obsessed, in love with herself, arse-kissing creep as he was. He could let love and his children go so easily but not the drugs, constantly snorting Mcat in the toilet cubicles, then having the absolute front to question and accuse others of substance use in the workplace the very same day he was doing it. He dropped everything in his life that should have meant something to him for a supervisor's role (a supervisor's role, people!), surrounding himself with people and stuff that he thought reflected the image of his role (again, for emphasis, a supervisor!) and even after four years he's never once looked as though he regretted any of his decisions. A truly dangerous individual I've done my best to stay away from.

All of them with the exception of Colin were the pettiest, most small-minded and deluded people I'd ever come across. They genuinely believed these little roles in a company tucked away in the middle of Nowheresville actually made them somebodies. Although it was pathetic to watch it play out every day, it couldn't be ignored as it was this pettiness, this scramble for scraps of synthetic power that made my life and the lives of many others so miserable; they weren't afraid to shame themselves, bend the rules, break the law or treat you badly if they thought it kept them in power. They were the wrong people for a leader's role, the last people I'd ever consider for such a responsibility but the perfect vessels for someone to carry out the plans of another small-minded idiot who should never have been anywhere near a position of authority.

## Rochelle

I've never in all my life met another woman like her.

I've always had the capacity to dislike others for the smallest or most bizarre things sometimes, even as petty as someone's laugh annoyed me once to the point, I actively avoided this particular woman at work, but it takes something or someone truly extraordinary for me to actually hate them. It's such a strong term and I'd never use it lightly and I never knew I was even capable of it until I met Rochelle. I wasn't alone in my opinion of her. No one in the business could stand her, apart from the odd one or two that had something to gain by her presence, of course. The directors liked her attitude, the way she chased after the results she'd promised them, but that was the full extent of their tolerance. They had no time for this woman beyond the professional scope because they knew just how manipulative she could be. Truly such a cold, cold woman but you'd never think it to look at her. She had a very quiet and almost vulnerable-looking demeanour and she also possessed a very warm-looking smile for anyone who was brave enough to make eye contact with her, but beneath that warm smile was a lion ready to pounce. She was in her mid-forties and stood five and a half feet tall. She was always smartly dressed, always wearing pencil skirts pulled well above the knee with a suit jacket to match it. She always wore knee-high leather boots to finish it all off and I must say, physically, Rochelle always looked very good. Her body was in great shape and the clothes she wore complemented her figure well. She had long, brown hair, healthy and full but sometimes she allowed it to get very greasy as if she didn't wash it from one week to the next and she also had a beautiful olive-looking skin tone.

I'd say the only problem she had in terms of her physical appearance was that she possessed the nose of an eighty-year-old man that seemed to consume over half her face from every angle you saw her. No matter how she dressed her schnoz always drew the eye before anything else, which must have frustrated her because she put so much effort into her sexy/professional image and the only thing she stood out for was the massive beak on her boat race! She must have been aware of it; we all were, and we never felt bad for mentioning it among one another because she was a horrible human being and it made us feel a little bit better when having to put up with her dictatorship.

She was a very arrogant woman, desperate to prove her worth from the get-go but she never got her own hands dirty. Employment, hiring and firing, welfare, rapport (or lack of), even the effort to know the names of her staff all left to her minions, they were all things beneath her as far as she was concerned.

She was a line/department manager, that was all, still bloody junior management, but she tried to behave as though she was some sort of director. She was my immediate manager and I'd only ever spoken to her twice in four years, twice! And each time she struggled to remember my name as she did everybody else's; we meant absolutely nothing to her.

She promised the seniors/directors when she took charge a ten per cent minimum increase in production over a three-year phased plan but never told them what the phases would be. Keeping the phases vague to the board left them to believe she could be implementing incentives and motivational techniques but the reality was her methods were bullying, humiliation, withdrawal of perks, break cuts, intimidation and breaking the law, all negative actions covered over by business phrasing with words like streamlining and reviewing. Assuming time and money saved from making cutbacks would take the business forward, she let years of company and product experience leave as a result and she also believed the parting experience wouldn't have a major impact on the running of the business, but it did. Failures, product issues and other problems went up as a result of her decisions, but rather than take any responsibility she pinned it all on the attitudes of the leaving employees. These people didn't leave because of the changes! They didn't leave because they didn't like Rochelle or her style of managing others, they left because they had no loyalty to the business! They left in droves, all at the same time after her takeover, because they were all chasing better money at other companies despite being with this one for many years with no previous desires to leave. It was never Rochelle's fault, it was always them, always something wrong with the parting employees. Change was needed and Rochelle was the martyr to bring about this change while everybody upped and left because they couldn't do what was necessary for the sake of the business, taking experience and solutions with them and using poor Rochelle as an excuse for going. She could spin a great story to sugar-coat her awful ideas and bad management, but the directors seemed to buy it each time and never looked past her word.

When the results and increases didn't come through by squeezing every last drop of blood from the staff that stayed for three years, her career plateaued. There's no doubt in my mind she took the manager role because she thought it would lead to better opportunities in the future, but her career is going nowhere now.

She is the worst manager that I've ever worked for because she's a ladder climber at best, and a terrible one. An arrogant, stubborn and selfish big-nosed bitch that made so many people suffer so many different things they shouldn't have in a workplace, making people lose their jobs, suffer bullying and exploitation all because she wanted these people to go because they didn't suit her stupid, half-thought ideals of work and all so she could chase a position the next level up that was never going to come to her. There is only one direction this corporate cum bucket should be heading for and that's the door as soon as the owners discover how much of the business she has rotted from the inside, but they still haven't. How long it's going to take for them to realise she's destroying them is anyone's guess.

Repeated product launch failures, products going out the door cheap, half-built and broken, years of experience leaving the business, record staff turnover rates, a lack of training and leadership throughout the whole department and very little production increase for all the sacrifices she's made others go through, the alarm bells continue to stay silent for now. I can only think the owners are continuing to swallow her bullshit or she's still swallowing their old man spunk.

Thomas

Ah, the man at the very top of the production heap, which is where all the problems began.

He was in charge of the entire company's production. Two hundred staff split over three different warehouses in two different locations within the same town. He was supposed to be the link between us at the bottom of the pile and the owners at the top.

The owners, despite all of their business successes, always made the time in the past to come and speak to the guys and girls on the front line of their business but they were getting old and wanted to take a step back from it and brought Tom in to be that part they could no longer fulfil. The brothers (owners) knew how much the people in the warehouse mattered and always did their best to make every one of them feel valued and like part of the family, not just because it was good practice and good business sense to keep employees' spirits up with praise or polite conversation; family was also a big part of the image they sold along with the product. Tom was supposed to continue with this approach. He'd been with the company for over fifteen years and by all accounts he was a pretty decent guy and a good director to work for.

He was a very short and small man in his late forties, who loved to talk about his amateur rugby and refereeing career, probably all to make up for his lack of physical stature. For the rugby fans among you, definitely a nine (scrum half) but wasn't enough of a gobshite so took up refereeing it instead. He had silver hair with large, thick, black eyebrows that took up half of his tiny forehead which removed the focus from his small, brown eyes and blotchy, pink skin complexion. Thomas was very well spoken. He had been public schooled and had a slightly posh accent. He always wore brand name, expensive designer shirts but never a tie. Tailor-made trousers but he never wore a belt or braces either and always wore comfortable-looking and smart, shiny shoes (no safety boots, he never went on the line). It was clear from his appearance he was one of the "higher ups" but insisted on a smart/casual dress among his office staff as well as himself in an attempt to put everyone at ease and create an environment where everyone appeared to be on an equal footing.

When I first began at this place, I would often see him walking around on the shop floor talking and engaging with the staff. He knew most of the production operatives on a first name basis and genuinely seemed to take an interest in their wellbeing. The problem he had in the role began a few months before I joined. The production manager in the position below him was going. He was off to advance his career by securing his own director's role at another company still working in production. A fantastic manager by all accounts that worked well with the whole team, had their respect, worked really well with Tom and was leaving a rather large pair of shoes to fill, and it's who wanted to fill those shoes that was the problem. A woman by the name of Rochelle was working in the purchasing department at the time that wanted the manager's position. She had absolutely no production experience, no qualifications or knowledge for the job but she did have two huge advantages over most of the candidates applying for it.

The first one was that she was Austrian and spoke fluent German. Austria and Germany were the two biggest markets for the products we provided. Although she had a very basic role in purchasing there were many occasions where she was pulled away from her normal role to help translate, interact and close deals with clients visiting from those countries. Her cultural understanding of German business and the relationships she formed with some of them had made her, in the eyes of the owners, a very valuable asset.

The rumours that she would leave the company to pursue a manager's job elsewhere if she was unsuccessful certainly caught the owner's attention. She wanted advancement and it was the only management role available to her in the business. And the second advantage? She was having an affair with Thomas. Both were married when it started, and they weren't exactly clever when it came to committing their adulterous sins. They'd been seen canoodling on many occasions by several members of staff in and out of work after hours, and Rochelle confiding in a few loudmouths and gossips in her department only confirmed what most knew or suspected. In fact, it seemed as though the only people that didn't know about their sordid, midlife fuck fest were their respective partners. Rochelle ended up leaving her husband and also broke up the affair with Thomas after he refused to leave his wife for her. This whole thing left Rochelle angry, bitter and resentful towards her former lover and she would have had no hesitations in blackmailing him over their poorly kept secret. Rochelle, unsurprisingly to everyone at the company, got the position after a few persuasive, and encouraging words from Thomas into the ears of the owners, promising to oversee her transition and development in like a mentor type of role making up for her lack of experience. From the moment Rochelle landed the job she felt as though she had to make an immediate impact to prove she was worthy of the position. She did everything in her limited knowhow to look competent, powerful and appear successful straight away making a load of stupid, half-baked choices knowing whatever policy change, decision or structural alteration she made would never be challenged by her immediate superior. The only thing Thomas could do was stand by and watch her make these ridiculous decisions she thought were amazing and revolutionary but were actually destroying the business he'd spent fifteen years helping to develop and expand. He was bent over a desk, so to speak, because he'd literally bent her over months before.

So Thomas, who once appeared to be a genuine and decent guy and a real company man (so I was told) ended up broken, powerless and pushed from his position out of fear of losing his wife over a very stupid decision he'd made months before. When he pulled his pants down for Rochelle, he never knew what the consequences would be, the safety and future of a business, the happiness and wellbeing of all the employees below him, their job securities as well as his marriage. He would keep his title for the time being and his salary, but he had lost his job. Rochelle wasted no time in pushing him to the shadows of the business and showing everybody who was really in charge.

# Chapter Seven

<u>What they did</u>

There was no time given or patience provided by the new gaffer to observe the day-to-day running of the business, get to know her new employees and see how efficiently the business was running before considering what changes, if any, she should make. She had an impact plan in her head and went about setting it up straight away without knowing anything about how the department functioned. She didn't even have a basic knowledge of the products we built. For Rochelle this was never about improvement or the company. It was nothing more than a shallow and ill-thought exercise to make it to the top of the chain without ever really thinking about the consequences of her actions.

First item on her list, she wanted her own people in the leader's roles below her. Established leaders already in the department posed a threat to her plans because they were strong, experienced and connected people that could and would challenge her decisions if they felt those decisions were bad for the department. She wanted a new, eager to please team in place, always keen to impress, and easy to manipulate and bend to her will. She forced the old line-leaders into quitting or stepping back down into production by amending their contracts (with enough legal notice) to take on a lot more responsibility with no extra pay to reflect it as well as being rude, constantly talking down to them and basically making the whole experience more stressful than it was worth. As all the line leaders' positions cleared, Rochelle gave the open slots to handpicked people from the production line that suited her alternative requirement and put them on a lot less money than their predecessors too. All health and safety, employment, holiday requests, training and development for over twenty members of staff each as well as the responsibility of making sure the production lines were churning out the ever-increasing targets were given to people who couldn't think for themselves and these idiots only received an increase in wages of about thirty pounds a week (before tax) from that of the production operators beneath them.

And for these leaders' positions she picked three of the most disruptive and ignorant people she could find from the warehouse, that's right, not the most ideal candidates for leadership, exemplary in their work ethic with attitudes and with the desire to want to help others. She deliberately picked three of the worst employees in her charge to step up to the role.

Rochelle knew she couldn't rid herself of all the bad apples from the business at the same time. Too much experience would walk away with them all at once and she was losing enough already, but she realised if she offered three of the thickest ego-driven morons a promotion it would rid the lines of the biggest disruption, keep some valuable knowledge still within the department and keep three people on whom she could manipulate and bend to her will. So, she picked Steve, Mathew and eventually Barry to be her line leaders. Three of the laziest operators in the building. They never hit targets, had very negative attitudes towards the company and dragged their heels with just about everything they were asked to do, they didn't care one bit. They were always on their phones, eating or constantly chatting to each other on the lines, forever distracted from their work and distracting others too by playing pranks or winding their colleagues up, forever trying their best to get a negative reaction from their teammates. Every time there was a meeting you could guarantee one of these three idiots would try to object in it or disrupt it regardless of the subject matter while they banged on about workers' rights and the fair treatment of all staff, which they knew very little about; it was all to be noticed as the bad boys of the warehouse and give their leaders chairing the meeting a hard time. They didn't really care for what they were disrupting.

They were the three dirtiest bastards in the place as well. Absolute fucking pigs when it came to their hygiene. They never wiped themselves clean, never washed their hands or their clothes and never covered their mouths or excused themselves in any way as they coughed, sneezed and spluttered all over the communal hand tools and other people. They thought it was hilarious when people complained to them about their visible spray going all over the equipment that had to be shared while at the same time refusing point blank to clean it up all in an effort to push for further reaction.

They were disgusting, entitled little fucktards who constantly mocked others and laughed at the disgust from their colleagues due to their vulgar behaviour. They were like schoolyard bullies ganging up on those around them who were weak or had clear vulnerabilities. A sad bunch of wet wipes who without each other would never dream of talking down to anyone, they were cowards. Rochelle had given them an extra couple of quid and a different coloured polo shirt to wear and this was enough to turn these pricks into the biggest hypocrites you could ever meet. They all instantly became grasses and snitches, the very thing they used to hate. They went from despising those who raised concerns about their drug abuse to dobbing on someone for chewing gum on the line to one of the supervisors. Once the three new line leaders were in place Rochelle then invented a new title of two positions below herself but above the line leaders and put them on the same salary as the old line-leaders she got rid of, roughly an extra hundred quid a week before tax. Jimmy, the last remaining old line-leader, was promoted to this spot quickly followed by Colin, employed from an external source. Their role was to oversee all of production as well as be a contact point for all the line leaders and aid them with their responsibilities as well as brief all the teams on business or policy updates while also dealing with all disciplinary and absence issues that arose. So, what the hell was Rochelle's job exactly then? I thought those things were what a line/department manager would take care of? That was the point of their very existence, wasn't it?

She distanced herself from the workers by creating an extra position beneath her own, then physically distanced herself by never speaking to her staff directly, unless they were sent to her office so she could deal with individual attitudes. It was pure divide and conquer. The workers always had safety in numbers before and were more inclined to stick up for one another in meetings and briefings because there was support on mass and they could challenge the manager face to face. The new way of getting the line leaders to make the announcements instead of her meant she was never answerable to what she was implementing and if there were any complaints, she wouldn't get the masses of comments coming her way all at the same time; she could pick off the natural leaders sent to her from the herd by the supervisors one by one if they disagreed with her plans, making issues that affected the whole team or department feel like individual battles against someone who orchestrated it all.

The first change to come in after the leaders — Rochelle banned all headphones from the warehouse. It pissed a lot of people off as pretty much everyone enjoyed plugging into their devices and escaping through their music, stories and podcasts. As much as it annoyed the staff and I really hate saying this, I could actually see her point on this one. It posed numerous health and safety issues; people moving around with various welding equipment, power tools and heavy goods while being distracted by loud noises being blown right into ears was just asking for trouble. Communication and focus also suffered, so it was fair enough as far as I was concerned, but it was a dog shit move to pull out so soon after being put in charge. It showed the intent early on that she had no concerns whatsoever about upsetting her staff to get what she wanted.

The next step was the complete banning of mobile phones on the shop floor. Mobiles were only to be used at break times from that point on. She did originally push for a complete ban of mobile phones from the building, everybody's phones to be stored in supplied lockers before the start of each shift but HR stepped in. They suggested with no point of contact and no direct phone line for family members to call into in case of an emergency it was an unethical move, so the change was restricted back as far as phones in break times only. The three worst offenders of phone use, Barry, Mathew and Steve, were the ones to brief it out, then enforce it despite the fact they continued to use their phones in work time. They got round it by saying they were technically non-production staff, therefore, the policy didn't affect them. They didn't care at all they were setting a double standard and rubbing it in their teams' faces. They policed the new phone rules by their unofficial strike policy. If you were seen on your phone, your name was recorded onto a spreadsheet on their computer. You were rarely told when your name was entered onto it and when it hit three occasions, they'd pull you into the office for a verbal warning, After a couple of verbal's you would then get a written warning, a couple of written warnings could result in temporary suspension or a full dismissal. I never used my phone on the line at work, but I found out I'd been given a strike by a colleague who spotted my name on the spreadsheet when peering over at Barry's desk. When I questioned Barry about this, he explained he'd seen me on the line taking my phone out of my front pocket and changing it over to one of the back ones. I explained to him that my phone was banging up against the counter I was working at and I simply moved it to the back pocket to prevent any damage to it and if he was indeed watching me like he'd claimed, he'd have seen the changeover was immediate and there was clearly no phone activity going on. His response was, "Well, you still got your phone out on the line."

"Yes, but not to use it, you said the use of mobile phones was prohibited and I didn't use mine. I took it out of my pocket and moved it. There was no phone use, Barry, it took about three seconds and I didn't even attempt to look at it."

"That's not my problem. Leave your phone in your pocket and there's no chance of you getting a strike, is there?"

"This is outrageous, Barry, I didn't use my phone, how can I appeal against this strike then?"

"You can't," he said, sniggering at my frustration before he walked off, what a knob! I didn't kick up a stink about it. No one would listen anyway even if I did. I knew I didn't use my phone on the line so the chances are it wouldn't happen to me again but I was quite pissed off about this dodgy, one-way, unclear system they were bringing in. It was never explained to us properly because it wasn't a real company policy. HR or the company had not approved it, I doubt they were even aware of it. It was something they invented to keep us on our toes and in check. The rules and recordings remained open to their interpretation and decision; in other words, if they really didn't like you, you could find your name going on that spreadsheet a lot more often.

Clocking-in cards were the next things to be implemented. Rochelle issued a brief to be given out by her leadership team. Anyone even a second late on the clock or to the morning meeting, which relied on the line leader's opinion of what was deemed as late to the meeting, and if you forgot your clock card once or it didn't work or register properly at the machine (you could never tell if it registered properly, it just beeped whether it worked or not as it was cheap), you guessed it, you'd get a strike. Same as before, verbal's leading to written warnings and all recorded on another spreadsheet. Loads of people ended up in the office over this one because the machine never bloody worked properly, the time was either wrong or it wouldn't register the card but the leaders were never interested in the reasons, they always found a way to make it our fault.

The uniform policy came in shortly after the clock cards.

Spending was cut back dramatically to two polo shirts or t-shirts, one pair of trousers and a pair of boots per year which is fair enough. If you have to cut back (which they didn't, they were extremely rich), you have to cut back. But if you went over budget through wear and tear or required something else like a woolly hat or a body warmer to wear in the winter, it was coming out of your pay packet. So you were left with a choice. Freeze yourself half to death in the middle of winter as the temperature indoors was almost as low as the temperature outdoors because the delivery bays were always open next to the production line, even though they were never supposed to be, sometimes even letting the snow through in the most extreme conditions, or be forced into buying their cheap, nasty uniform at your own expense. You couldn't wear your own hats or jackets to combat the cold from the bays that were never supposed to stay open, oh no. No matter how cold you were feeling, no matter how much you were shivering, it would result in a strike each time you wore a piece of your own clothing in order to protect yourself. This again pissed a lot of people off because contracted employees had to wear, and on occasion pay for, uniform, but the other forty per cent of the staff who were long-term agency were not provided any uniform and got to wear pretty much whatever they wanted within reason, so it wasn't as though the company clothes were providing some sort of unique protection, they just wanted those in permanent employment to look professional at all times, but they failed to see that dozens of employees shivering violently in the winter months didn't exactly put the company in a good light to any visitors or customers.

Every morning brief seemed to deliver some form of bad news or negative change for us, not trying to be dramatic or anything but it was never positive, no matter how hard we worked for the company or how much we achieved, nothing good ever came out of their mouths. More threats, more restrictions and it was gradually chipping away at our morale. Workers began speaking up in frustration at the line leader's morning briefs, objecting and becoming rather concerned by it all. They could see a hundred more little changes coming in like the ones we'd already been given and felt they had to say how it was affecting the mood and spirit of the teams. Of course, all these concerns, objections and countersuggestions were never listened to, line leaders had no power to change anything — they were merely sounding boards for Rochelle and so always ended the meeting with one of three of their favourite sayings:

"If you don't like it, go and find another job."

"That's just the way it is now and it's not going to change."

"If you don't adopt the changes, there will be consequences."

The ones that constantly showed their concerns in these morning briefings became the targets for Rochelle and her team. They were an inconvenience for her and they had to be rid of by any means necessary.

There was a young man by the name of Dean. A yoga-loving vegetarian festival nut who resided in a mobile home just down the road from the warehouse. He was constantly being sent up to Rochelle's office over his "attitude" because he spoke up in the morning briefs and he didn't mince his words in her office either. He always told Rochelle (I know because I was a witness to some of these meetings) how others were being verbally abused and shouted at by the line leaders and expressed how he felt some of the staff had been made to leave through made-up accusations of racism and sexism to which only the line leaders were witnesses to said incidents. He also always raised the point in these office call ups that all the changes she made only ever affected the staff at the very bottom, never the supervisors or the line leaders — they continued to do whatever they wanted. Rochelle couldn't handle his questions. He was direct, and she didn't like it at all, she wasn't used to it. She was used to kiss ups saying yes all of the time, so with Dean she would get angry, snappy and flustered by his honest and blunt approach knowing she could never provide a reasonable response that would satisfy him. Instead, she responded by talking down to him and tried to bypass his concerns and when that failed to work, she decided it was time for him to go.

The line leaders began pulling him in the office over anything and everything, however slight, however small. Lateness, a couple of seconds here or there on occasion, phone use (line leaders making up most of these incidents that couldn't be argued or proved) and toilet breaks, length and frequency of visits remaining unspecified by the accusers.

He was by no means the worst operator for all the things listed above but his flaws were useful to their cause. Those who were friends of the management or sucked up to them enough were overlooked but poor old Dean was neither.

They bombarded him almost every day with bollockings and dressing downs. Then eventually they moved onto written warnings and notes for his file knowing his severe dyslexia stifled him. Sure, they offered the services of HR to assist with reading and understanding what was going on, but they couldn't advise on what he could do. Every time he came out of the office, he looked confused and bewildered with what was happening. He didn't know any of his rights or how he could challenge the false accusations in a formal meeting, he didn't have a clue where to begin and as company policy dictated, he wasn't allowed to openly discuss what was said in the meetings (although he did), forced into a place of no support. It all went over his head and he never appealed against a single claim, even the bullshit ones, and eventually they sacked him knowing it would never be contested at any level internally or externally, not for an entry level production job by someone struggling with the laws and who no longer wanted to be there anyway.

The next change brought in Rochelle removed all interviewing or applying for a position in her department. Everything was to go through the temp agencies. This ensured very loose and open contracts that could be terminated for any reason. If you didn't learn quick enough and with some of the work being quite intricate or you weren't fast enough after just a few days or your face didn't fit, they got rid of you with no more legal obligations or contractual issues. They managed to find a loophole for the shit they were doing anyway and very soon after it made way for an army of spineless, submissive cowards to come into the warehouse because if you showed any kind of strength or leadership as a temp, you were gone. If you answered back to the bullying from the line leaders or you questioned anything at all, you were gone.

The turnover of staff for such a small place was incredible. Five a week on occasion and in a warehouse of only seventy to eighty shop floor workers it was quite a significant number. The ones that remained after this process were the most introverted people you could meet. They rarely spoke, let alone raised an opinion and dared not raise their head to an order, no matter how unreasonable, and some were absolute boot lickers on top of it. It was sickening to watch some of them, full grown men and women behaving like lapdogs to horrible people who bathed in the attention. These were the candidates lucky enough to be offered a one-year contract after a time but only a year to begin with, mind! The first contract was to make sure that the behaviour all the leaders observed from the temps wasn't just a showpiece to land the job. When the year was up, if you hadn't put a toe out of line or your tongue was brown enough, they'd take you on, but that was a rarity. If you took a couple of days sick in the year (well within the policy) or were late once or twice or you grew in any kind of confidence, they cut you off.

A slow feed of doormats was dripping into the business while good workers, natural leaders and grafters were shown the door because in one way or another they highlighted the insecurities and flaws of those in charge. To work well was fine; to outshine your superior wasn't tolerable.

The absence policy was changed next. She shortened the periods of sickness to the absolute minimum legal requirement for each stage of the absences to get rid of what she called the "freeloaders". One being a pleasant but rather soft man in his mid-forties trying to hold down a full-time job as well as looking after his terminally ill wife. This gentleman had an agreement with the old manager that if he should be called away to tend to some of his wife's needs about five minutes' walk away down the road, then he could make back the time when he could or take the time unpaid and in a twenty-four-hour factory, why the hell not? What an impossibly sad situation to deal with for any marriage or family! He rarely had any time off before this. Surely it was the very least they could do for a good, hard-working employee with a decent track record who had fallen into really crap circumstances?

Rochelle used the new absence policy to get rid of this guy for being one of his wife's carers. She removed his word agreement of flexi-time with the old manager and replaced it with a marked absence every time he had to leave to go and be with his partner. Which, of course, kept happening as her illness progressed until eventually, he'd gone past the final written warning and was let go by the company. Whether he had a good legal position or not I'm afraid I don't know, but just like Dean, life was too busy and funds were too low for him to contest a job that brought in a basic salary and was changing into an environment that he no longer liked.

There is something on the company's updated policy that states leniency can be given in exceptional circumstances regarding absence from work. This was to make sure as a business and from a legal standpoint they always had some wriggle room on difficult cases and also to demonstrate they were capable of compassion under certain situations. How was this situation not exceptional? I've never in all my time there seen it used once at ground level but Jimmy and the other leaders reaped the benefits of the policy's flexibility on more than a few occasions, reminding us once more it was one rule for Rochelle's boys and a different one for us.

Break times were the next things to be targeted. Five minutes to be taken from each break in the shift as well as the five-minute pack up and personal locker time we had at the end of every day. It was all taken away and put towards production/build time. Rochelle was hoping to force the numbers up on targets this way. It didn't work. People were upset by the move and were reluctant to continue going the extra mile for the numbers like they used to, so even when the extra time was added the numbers worked out being the same as they were before; this was also a result from ever-changing, inexperienced staff coming onto the lines, and this didn't sit well at all with the ruthless cow upstairs in the office. This must have been the big part of her plan because when it didn't work, she threw her toys out of the pram, screamed, shouted and demanded the line leaders watched us all like hawks to see when and where the line was slowing down and "manage" the operators responsible for it. They obeyed, naturally, watched us and began pulling out the people they felt were responsible for the slowdown and grilled them over their performances. They always did this in pairs to outnumber the poor operator they were inaccurately accusing of slowing production down. They just ended up pulling out the more relaxed and competent workers from the line because they didn't look flustered or panicked by their presence and could cope easily with the workload. If you looked under pressure and were rushing around, they assumed that was a good sign, but more often than not they were the operators struggling. The whole exercise became completely redundant. The numbers stayed around the same. Everybody became less motivated to work because they were being challenged even if they worked well by twats who only knew how to isolate and intimidate them.

She then took the five-minute handwashing time away from the beginning of our lunch break and it still didn't have any impact on the figures. The only change that came was workers were going to break times without washing their hands in some sort of dirty protest, spreading germs, bacteria and dirt all over the poorly maintained canteen areas making break and lunch times a pretty grotty experience.

Rochelle had taken a total of twenty minutes personal time a day away from her staff to little effect in production and rather than learn the lesson that people who are forced into something will always drag their heels she kept the new times that way permanently, and I really believe she kept the new times purely out of spite because it didn't go how she intended.

After the break times she then began to dick around with the wages. She put a stop to the annual pay increase that always softened the blow of rising inflation (roughly about one percent a year) and the reason she could do this so easily is because we did have an excellent bonus system. The bonus system added approximately an extra hundred and fifty to two hundred pounds a month, an extra two thousand pounds a year. A substantial amount of money in relation to what we earned and yet it was left untouched. It all seemed too good to be a "Rochelleism". There was no way given her cutthroat attitude she would pick the more considerate and expensive option that benefitted us by not touching the bonus and, of course, she didn't. A couple of months after putting a stop on all wage increases, she pushed through a change to the bonus. She changed it from a performance bonus to a profit share scheme. This action removed up to seventy-five per cent of its value, cutting the annual bonus down to only five hundred pounds a year, if we were lucky. The scheme had also become subject to overtime spending, which meant the more overtime we had to do to make up the orders the less the bonus that month would be. Product development or machine replacement was also included in the bonus budget, which, of course, all happened frequently, meaning more often than not we fell short of the desired amount. By keeping this minimal bonus scheme in place, it meant they could continue to stop any wage increase because we were compensated in another way. This meant after a couple of years we would lose out in terms of increased overall wages and instead rely on a dwindling and fluctuating incentive, very harsh and very clever, hurting the biggest and last reason to turn up to any job.

Her self-importance grew as much as her frustrations did. Thinking she had become a bit of a dynamic mover and shaker with all of her "positive" alterations she decided she was too good to actually be associated with the very department she was supposed to run and moved her office out of the production area altogether and relocated to a bigger office near to the directors' offices area of the building.

It was truly pathetic to watch, to be honest. A desperate political and purely image-based move to look and act as a director. Swanning around the admin areas and lording over the office staff and engineers as though she was their boss too. She was trying to act like the owner when the owner wasn't looking, but as soon as the owners turned up for site visits, she would immediately start grovelling and hiding behind her low-level status, suddenly appearing out of nowhere onto the shop floor acting as though she was part of the team while desperately trying to remember the names of her staff.

With no presence or involvement apart from dishing out more restrictions, the day-to-day running passed completely over to Jimmy, Colin and the line leaders and with no brain cells, leadership or spines between them, they could only rely on the one thing they had been shown in their development, the do as I said or we will make your life difficult approach. And just like Rochelle this free rein, this unchecked authority began massively overinflating their egos and the perceptions of their own positions and importance to almost delusional levels. It was like watching school prefects trying to play headmasters. They fought, squabbled and stabbed each other in the back all to gain a little extra notice in the eyes of their manager at every opportunity. Their behaviour got worse and worse over time. They always relied heavily on each other to carry out their objectives but they could never trust one another knowing their colleagues could turn on them at any moment to get ahead in the game.

Although always preoccupied with office politics Rochelle would still manage the department to a degree, keep her hand in by calling the leaders into meetings in her office where she would dish out fresh objectives in line with her vision but left it entirely up to all of them how they got the results, making her able to turn a blind eye to their methods while constantly demanding that her targets were met.

The department continued to churn through staff. Dropping and sacking anybody who couldn't cope with the new and ever-rising demands or couldn't adhere to the almost impossible target hikes.

The box ticking always pissed me off on a personal level too. It constantly demonstrated their hollow and one-dimensional intentions to be recognised rather than be in the role for improvement and guidance, and I'll give you an example of this.

Rochelle set a task to her leaders to find improvements on the line to save time and speed up production (as though any operator weren't capable of making their own lives easier). Now there's no harm in the real world of constantly trying to improve the environment around you but sometimes failing because the room to improve just isn't there. If there was no obvious or visible improvement that could be made, I'm hoping most people in some sort of leadership role would have the honesty to put their hand up and say something like "there's no obvious improvements at this time" or something to that effect. Displaying strength, confidence and maintaining honesty between you and your superior.

With this bunch of clowns, failure was not an option, so as a result of this thinking they placed enormous pressure on themselves to succeed whatever the cost to the people working below them. Some changes that were made to the lines actually caused more hassle or work for the operators, but if a visible change was clear, the leaders could dress it up as an improvement on the production line even if it placed a greater demand on the staff. By selling these changes as time savers it meant Rochelle would also put the targets up on the line and the operators were put under even greater pressure, having to build faster with no improvements actually being made.

One particular line, built foot pads for chairs for the elderly or disabled to rest their legs on wheelchairs. Rochelle demanded that the leaders improved the production speed of this line as they weren't turning out enough products every day to fulfil the orders. The leaders held numerous meetings in the office or on the line almost daily about ideas or potential changes to the line while never bothering to ask the operators who worked there every day what their ideas were. They spoke about the operators, spoke over them and in front of them while never actually including them in any talks. After weeks of observing, reviewing and holding meetings trying desperately to find an improvement they were still scratching their empty, thick and arrogant heads as to what they could do, so they made something up instead.

The packing area of this particular line had one operator that stood right at the end. His or her job would be to simply pack the finished products into a pre-made box that they'd put together while the operators built the product, put a label on the box, seal it and place it onto a pallet on the floor right next to them. When the pallet was full (about twenty boxes) the packer would take the pallet up to the distribution area, grab a fresh, empty pallet, bring it back to the line and begin filling it again. The line produced about eighty of these sets of pads a day (four pallets). The line leaders in their desperation moved this pallet six inches closer to the packer and went completely nuts over it! They held meetings with Rochelle about how it improved general manual handling for the operator, how it improved on packing times, therefore freeing up time for the packer to take a bit more of the build from the stage/operator before them as part of their responsibility and share a more equal part of the build and therefore speed up the whole process over all. Six inches of movement was supposed to have done all that when in reality it did fuck all! They put the targets up by another eight a day under rigged build timings all over a pallet placement, something that made absolutely no difference at all. Rochelle got her target increase, the line leaders got their recognition and a pat on the head and the poor operators that were overlooked through the whole process were forced to work harder to hit the adjusted targets or face performance review meetings, basically to threaten them with the sack if they didn't build faster.

Colin, Jimmy and their cronies applied this kind of made-up, box-ticking bullshit to every single line over the whole of the production, making everybody's lives more stressful and more pressured just to appear like dynamic innovators instead of having to face honesty and be perceived as a failure in their boss's eyes.

The next step was the crackdown on health and safety. I

say crackdown, what I actually mean was they manipulated health and safety to suit their reporting targets. The reporting of incidents needed to increase in the warehouse to reflect the company's desire to constantly improve safety for all its employees. Rochelle set her own targets once more; this time it was for all her leaders to report a certain number of incidents each month. This was interpreted by the leaders to report anything and everything to bump the numbers up, no matter how small or in some cases non-existent, totally undermining the purpose of the whole process. They weren't interested in safety at all, they were interested in looking as though they were, so lying, forging and inventing became the tools to create the impression that suited the company image.

If there was a two-inch bit of cardboard waste accidently dropped in the walkway on its way to recycling, it was reported even though it was never reported the thousand times it had happened before. So much time wasted in form filling and risk assessments which took time to write, hand in and process for improvement instead of stopping, bending over and picking up a bit of cardboard and asking the operators to be a bit more mindful was fucking ridiculous. The result? The preventative measure after all their paperwork? To brief out to the team not to drop cardboard, not to be more mindful but not to drop cardboard like we were so thick we didn't know not to drop cardboard. Of course, we knew not to drop the fucking little bit of cardboard on the way to the recycling bin. When you're asked to take huge stacks of waste at a time it's going to happen. For anyone who does the laundry in the house knows from time to time a small sports sock is going to drop off the pile somewhere in transit. It's annoying; you don't want it to happen as you've got to go all the way back down the stairs to pick up one tiny sock, but it happens. When you notice it, you're going to pick it up, you don't make a big deal out of it, stop, fill out a form and hand it in to your partner to risk assess it — you pick it up and get on with it! You don't need someone briefing you at home not to drop your sock because it will happen from time to time and you will pick it up as soon as you see it. Now before you even begin to argue that this is health and safety and it might seem pointless but it's all part of the process, you could well be right, but to pick and choose what was reported and what wasn't certainly isn't health and safety, no matter what your stance. They were always hard and vigilant every time they saw a bit of cardboard on the floor or a bin starting to overflow, but when a young, perfectly healthy young lady in her mid-twenties fainted at work, what do you think they did? You guessed it, they turned a blind eye to it and pretended it wasn't happening, not a single form filled out or even a comment to the health and safety manager. Why, if they were so hot on it? Firstly, because they were encouraged to report the risks, not actual incidents, and no one wanted to be the leader making Rochelle appear less than perfect. Secondly, they knew the conditions at work could have been a contributing factor. She collapsed in the middle of a heatwave and the warehouse felt like you were walking into an oven every day of it, no air conditioning, just fans blowing hot air around an intense environment. Constant pressure to work faster and abuse every time you went to hydrate yourself all added up to trouble in any potential investigation carried out. No leader wanted to reveal the truth of the situation so they got the first aiders to patch her up, check her over and get her back on the line as soon as possible without a single word of it ever being written.

# Chapter Eight

A year and a half later

Eighteen months after her take-over we never saw Rochelle at all. Anybody starting fresh in the department after that time had no idea who she was or what she did despite her being the line manager.

I did cover in the previous chapter that she removed herself from the department and put herself in a director's office, but we did still see her after the move from time to time even if it was for only a split second. Being an absolute chain-smoker, she used to walk through the warehouse en route to one of her eight daily cigarette breaks. It used to be her thirty-second slot to appear in the warehouse and pick fault in the operators and complain if she saw something that wasn't to her liking in half a minute's assessment or update a leader on a new change as they followed her around, practically making love to her shadow as she strutted around the place, but she never ever spoke to any of us directly. With her hierarchy well established, she was too big to associate herself with us. Fast forward eighteen months and she didn't even strut through the shop floor any more. She took a longer alternative route for her fag breaks. She realised that all her changes, cutbacks and alterations to the running of the department were never going to deliver the ten percent increase she had promised the directors and being the arrogant piece of shit she was, she most likely blamed us for a fictitious incompetence rather than take a long hard look in the mirror to find the answer to her problems and so avoided us completely. To her, it was our fault we weren't inspired or motivated to give more than the absolute minimum after stripping us of every privilege and expecting us to do more than before.

Whether she liked it or not we were still her employees and so she had to still demonstrate some sort of interest in us, but it was reluctant at best. Almost like a spoiled child being made to join in with her friends at the party when all she really wanted to do is sit in the corner of the room and sulk with her arms crossed and wearing an angry and grumpy face at the realisation her party and presents didn't meet her unbelievable expectations.

She still found the time and ways to take things from us, though, but it wasn't about saving money or making herself look good by this point, it was about nothing but spite because we weren't delivering her vision of change and promise.

Example, she began targeting things as petty as "the grey roll". Well, it wasn't actually named grey roll but that's just what we called it. It was a large kitchen roll, paper-like material, but it was light grey and double the roll size and it was used for everything in the day-to-day running of the business. They were stored in plastic dispensers on the walls of all the production lines and in the canteen areas and it was very handy stuff indeed. We used it to wipe down dirty products before being packed, clean the hand tools on occasion and mop up all spillages and clean the lines down with them when they were dirty. Despite its regular use in a twenty-four-hour factory with over seventy staff we probably used about five or six rolls of this stuff a week, so not a great deal. Can't imagine for a multimillion-pound company that it was a massive cost, but she banned it, why? At most it was about a grand or two a year in cost and it really helped with sending clean products out the door, but it wasn't banned for that. She noticed one or two people using it to blow their noses if they were running because of the cold conditions in the winter and a few using them as makeshift napkins when they were eating greasy food. She wasn't prepared to pay towards these minimal, unnecessary costs which equated to nothing more than a few hundred pounds for noses a year at best, so she refused to buy any in, insisting that everybody bring their own napkins in when eating and their own handkerchiefs when having to wipe themselves, because essentially, they worked in a fridge. Pure spite, she did it to make everyone's lives that bit more difficult, but it didn't work. What the staff no longer used in "grey roll" they used in company toilet paper instead and it probably ended up more costly because people were leaving the line each time to tend to their paper needs rather than the "grey roll" being at their disposal, products were going out the door totally filthy leading to complaints and returns from contracts, which was a very expensive process. Eventually she had to concede and bring the rolls back into the warehouse, but she made sure the leaders used their valuable time and made them monitor exactly how it was used each time and report every time it wasn't used for purpose. It never worked; everyone still blew their noses on it.

Another example would be her attempt to make us sift through the dirt of the warehouse in the pursuit of lost or dropped screws. The odd nut or bolt was dropped from time to time where we were under a constant pressure to build faster.

Some of them were lost and some were just thrown to the floor where the bolt or nut had rounded in the build, so broken parts were being deposited on the floor along with the occasional lost working part by operators too lazy to throw it in the bin. Rochelle and Barry had somehow come to the conclusion that as a business we were dropping nearly two hundred thousand pounds in parts every year. That equated to about seven hundred and fifty pounds a day lost by being dropped on the floor by less than a hundred workers with screws that equated to pennies at a time, really? Not very likely or it would have been raining metal droplets all day. What's more likely is Barry, who was in charge of stock control, fucked up somewhere on the stock orders and lost some, so decided to shift the blame on the operators for profit lost and Rochelle jumped at his idea of how to correct it. We were told every day when we swept up, that everything we cleaned up, was to be gathered into a large yellow plastic tub put at the end of the line and at the end of the week we were to sift through this dirt and rubbish with our bare hands to retrieve these dropped parts. The only thing that stopped this deluded bitch from going through with this absurd and ridiculous idea was the health and safety manager. One of the operators, and quite rightly concerned for his wellbeing, went and spoke to the health and safety manager about the issue. As soon as he was made aware of her plans, he told Rochelle that this would not go ahead because of the health risks it posed to the operators. Rats crawled around on the shop floor and urinated and defecated all over the place and it exposed us to a lot of potential diseases if we started sorting our way through the dirt. Rochelle hated being told no, especially after she'd already promised the change. The poor operator who raised his concerns to the H & S manager was put on a verbal warning for leaving his line without seeking permission from one of the line leaders rather than being thanked for doing the right thing.

Petty moves from a petty woman that went nowhere. It was her determination to make our lives miserable and uncomfortable. Nothing else could have been gained by her actions. She constantly thought up and threw out new ideas like this to punish us while appearing to take enjoyment from it going by her smug reactions, all while focusing on her new project.

Knowing she was failing in her promises to the directors with regard to the target increases, she latched onto a new area of the business in order to save some face, her reputation (what there was of it) and her job. She managed to force herself into the new product launch. Now unfortunately I can't tell you what the new product was without giving away who the company is. It's just too obvious, but I can tell you it wasn't a brand-new product at all — it was just sold that way to rejuvenate the company's image and make them competitors in their market once more, it was just an old product rehashed and to everybody else in the industry it was bloody obvious too! Rochelle figured if she could latch herself onto the success of this product launch, she'd receive some kudos, no matter how undeserving it was, and save her position. So she resorted to some of her old tricks once more to accomplish this and began an affair with the head of engineering and development just like she did with Tom. Once she was in and had a hold over him, she began imposing herself into his department straight away. Telling his engineers what to do and how to do things with absolutely no knowledge or understanding of their profession. Forcing them to work with line leaders with regard to product development and the occasional operator who sucked up to her massively and possessed no real opinion of their own whatsoever. Honestly, these carefully selected operators could have seen her spray a dog turd gold and they'd have said "yes, this is going to work" every time; absolutely sickening to observe them lie time and time again all because they were too scared to go against their gut and tell the truth, that the project was a piece of shit, it wasn't going to work and it was potential embarrassment for the company. She basically poisoned the whole project from the start as the head of engineering could only stand and watch out of fear of being revealed as a cheat and to no surprise the "new" product would go on to fail. Just a week before its release they pulled the plug on the whole project.

But what's important to the story is that this kept her totally away from production, giving her leadership team almost total control of the department in her absence and they were absolutely abusing the opportunity they were given.

Steve had become disenchanted with the whole "success" thing at this point. After the novelty had worn off of being promoted and the momentum of climbing up had stopped, mixed with the fact that the other leaders were ganging up on him and throwing all their failures at his feet, he became deeply depressed and was signed off from work. He'd burned bridges with all of his old friends for a status that amounted to nothing more than a supervisor role and all his "new" mates had turned on him and stabbed him in the back. Steve had become isolated and stale from the leadership pack and had become a bit of a loner on his return. I really wanted to feel sorry for him and on the very odd occasion I guess I did because I could see how vulnerable he'd become. He had turned into a broken and miserable man, but whatever pity I did have towards him on those occasions wouldn't last very long. I could never forget when things seemed to be going well for him and he thought he was on top, he was quite happy to trample on anyone he was supposed to have cared about, and I had no doubt if the chips would have fallen back the other way again in the future, he would do exactly the same again, he was only capable of looking out for himself. That's who he was now, naive, shallow, petty and weak.

As for the rest, Jimmy, Mathew and Barry, I'll start by telling you they were all openly doing drugs, on occasion at work. Mathew had never hidden his party lifestyle. Constantly bragging about his drug-fuelled benders and weekends away in Amsterdam to sleep with prostitutes to anyone who was forced to listen. Jimmy didn't surprise me at this point either. He was that fucking selfish to drop his kids, and pick up drugs, to pursue a life he wanted. I saw it coming, but Barry, the married, repressed lizard did shock me a little.

Cocaine, the "glamorous" drug to reflect their "successful" lifestyles, Marijuana and even Mcat. How do I know all of this? Well, firstly, it was easy to spot. I'd been around enough users in my time at various parties, social events and even down the local pub to know when somebody had shoved something up their nostrils. Always loud, obnoxious, oblivious, rude fuck monkeys over-socialising and enjoying their own worlds rather than the company they were in. It was also obvious when these idiots weren't on it. Sniffing their noses up and clearing their throats constantly like something was stuck back there, looking physically tired but wiry whilst trying their utmost to appear normal by burying their anxieties and twitches in the workplace as best as they could. They overcompensated in every engagement with another member of staff above or below them by talking too much or overemphasising and remained totally oblivious to the fact they stuck out like a sore thumb looking pale and sweaty every minute of the day.

Secondly, I saw them all at various times scoring and collecting drugs from the few dodgy and well-connected employees that remained in the company. Quiet and nervous hand exchanges in toilets and locker rooms when they thought no one was looking. Thirdly, I caught Jimmy topping up on a bit of "meow meow" in the fucking toilet cubicle. I heard him snorting it one morning as I waited in the toilets for the first available cubicle. He came out and freed up the first one for me and he smelled as though a bunch of cats had just pissed all over him; it was a truly disgusting and pungent smell. I stepped past him to enter the cubicle he had just come from to find residue of a whitish looking powder on the top of the toilet roll holder. He was too fucking lazy or high to clean up after himself properly. Fourthly, and most importantly, one of the girls Mathew and Barry were grooming told me all about the drug taking going on in her house before and after they used her.

When left totally in charge Barry and Mathew in particular used their position to bed young, and in some cases vulnerable, young women who came in from the agency. Two men in their thirties, one a disgusting, forceful blob of shit, the other a married, cocky prick, used the company's employment process to target impressionable women looking for job security by offering permanent contracts (one-year contracts first) to those who would "go the extra mile" for them. Eighteen, nineteen, completely fresh into the work environment and the adult world, they didn't care, in fact the fresher the better, as they were often easier to mould and manipulate. As well as all the gossip surrounding this particular issue, I'd personally observed a few cases myself and they all started exactly the same way. As soon as they saw a young girl sent in by the agency, they would immediately go over to her and switch on their poor attempt at charm even if the woman wasn't on their line. It didn't stop either of them approaching the new target. They'd show off in front of these women, talking down to other staff members in front of them, shout at them, order them to do menial tasks like sweeping up or getting parts even when these tasks weren't required as a way of flexing their managerial muscles and displaying dominance in front of the newbie. If the girls responded to this in a positive way, then the leaders would take this as a sign of approval rather than politeness and persist by spending hours of each day gently breathing down their victims' necks while telling shit jokes and getting ego boosts and stimulation from the fake or put-on laughs from nervous young girls who weren't sure how to handle such bulldozing advances. After a few weeks of constantly sniffing around them, if the girls suddenly backed off because they realised the intentions of their supervisors, then they too would back off and most likely get rid of the girl who rejected them, but if the temp continued to play up to their attention, then things would progress. They would tell the "girls" that they were working well even if they were completely useless (making all of us pick up their slack on the line) and invite them out for drinks, and by drinks I don't mean with anyone else in a social gathering like a night on the town — it would be with just Barry and Mathew. Drinks would lead to pre-planned advances, sex and affairs; the crappy contract offers would come out after to keep the women sweet.

One girl spilled the beans on it all to me and her name was Rebecca. A troubled nineteen-year-old girl who arrived at the company already loaded with a troubled past. Very sweet but a bit ditzy, very friendly but clearly very vulnerable due to a broken home life provided by her parents and was the perfect target for those letches' horrible intentions. When she first started at the company, she was quite endearing. Being placed closely to me on the line I befriended her in a strictly professional capacity, of course, and we got along very well. A very beautiful, intelligent and bright woman who probably should have been destined for a higher education at college or university level but the death of a close friend the year before had hit her hard and a previous addiction to hard drugs had caused her a world of chaos, psychologically speaking. A "normal" job, whether long or short term seemed like a good way to add stability, routine and perspective for somebody who found themselves struggling so soon into adult life.

I've no doubt in the right environment Rebecca could have turned her life around. She screamed potential in every way through her personality and ability to learn quickly but her further misfortune was that she turned up at the wrong place. You think Barry or Mathew give a single toss about her past and problems? Not one, they only saw a beautiful and vulnerable woman they could target for sex. Within a couple of weeks, they began sniffing around her as a team, trying to impress her, over-flirting and constantly asking inappropriate questions like "Do you have a boyfriend?", "Do you live on your own?", "You ever taken coke?", "Are you still a virgin?" When I pointed out their behaviour was completely inappropriate, rather than back off and realise they were clearly overstepping the mark they moved her away from me onto another line where she was almost alone except for two or three other people who lacked the courage to say anything to them. They had gained complete control of her and the area she was in. After a few more weeks of flattering her and wearing her down through promises of a good time, job opportunities and a party lifestyle that played to her vulnerabilities she finally caved in.

The flat that she rented alone became the venue for their exploitations as they encouraged her to take drugs once more, snorting off her coffee table and smoking weed in her living room. On many occasions these "parties" eventually turned into cheap drug-filled exchanges. Sex in exchange for more drugs to satisfy her refuelled addiction turning her into a distant, angry and detached human being.

A typical "party" would end up consisting of Barry and Mathew turning up to her house together, sitting in her tiny living room putting crap in their systems and listening to music, then, once they were high enough, they would take it turns to take her into her own room and have sex with her and leave various drugs on her bedside table as payment for their release. She would be led by the hand one at a time where she would go in, lie back, insist the lights were kept off and let them do what they wanted while she took it lifelessly. When one was finished, she would go to the bathroom, clean herself up and the other one would go in and do the same.

She confessed this all to me over lunch breaks, sometimes while she was still high, an apprentice at the company who lived in the same block of flats who was also besotted with her confirming their arrival and uncomfortable noises coming from her flat.

I was sick to my stomach by the things she told me and her story haunts me to this day. Not only by the awful circumstances they'd pushed on this young girl but the way I'd observe these monsters at work immediately after one of their gatherings. Laughing, joking and fooling around with each other and other leaders like they were in a fucking little boys' club while still continuing to give people beneath them a hard time as if what they were doing to her and others was fine. I begged Rebecca on numerous occasions to go to HR or the police and tell them everything, even offering to go with her and support her through the process, but she never did, she didn't want to. She was too scared to go, plus if the sex stopped, so did the drugs, and by that point she was hooked again.

Although our experiences were worlds apart, our circumstances were aligned in certain ways. The ship was so tight there that any visits off the line to the HR department were monitored by the very people you wanted to report, plus they had brought in a no-wandering rule meaning if you went offline without authorisation, you'd get a strike. They knew exactly who went where at all times and would have a pretty good idea of what could be said as well as the fact the HR department was under Rochelle's influence, so you couldn't trust in confidentiality. They had the process of reporting anything firmly locked down. If Rebecca or I had exposed them, you could guarantee they'd either work it out and then make our lives miserable until we quit or they would try and sack us over something they could make stick.

This whole situation raised real moral questions for me. I was horrified by what was going on and really wanted to help

Rebecca and her situation despite the fact she was reluctant to help herself and yet at the same time I found myself frightened at the prospect of losing my job when work was becoming a little harder to find.

How fucked up is that? Really! What a sorry piece of shit argument to excuse myself from responsibility in this horrible mess.

For years looking from the outside of these situations that I'd see in the newspapers or on the tele about grooming or corruption I had such a black and white moral stance on it. If I saw something unjust, I would do the right thing and report it, it's as simple as that. Why don't people ever say anything? I would straight away. It's just single minded and selfish to look at our own potential individual sufferings than to do the right thing! Well, I didn't. I was afraid and I was a coward at that time and no matter how much time passes there's no running away from it. I was too scared to speak my mind and take them on, just like the rest of the staff around me who all saw it too and did nothing. I felt isolated, divided from any support at work; taking them on as an individual would only land me out of a job at the end of it with no consequences to them whatsoever. It began to plague me every day after she told me. I'd seen what they were doing to her and others and felt so ashamed of myself for letting it continue. I began drinking heavily most nights, sometimes up to two bottles of red wine a night, not to escape any pain or block out what was happening — it was pure shame, self-destruction, I was breaking myself up over my own conscience. A couple of months passed and every day I had to witness this poor girl deteriorate a little more as they stood there almost looking proud and smug of what they were doing. They appeared to be untouchable and it was pissing me off, not just the protection afforded to them but the fact they had the will to do something so damaging without giving it a second thought.

One evening on a weekend I drank myself into an absolute stupor and laid out everything that was going on to a friend. I decided after her advice and when I sobered up that I would write an anonymous letter to HR and post it posing as a temp that had left the company explaining absolutely everything about Rebecca's situation, the drugs, the sexual exchanges, the grooming, everything, with a clear message that although I had left, I still had informants within the company and if no visible action was taken, I would notify the police. I took all the necessary precautions, I asked my friend to type up the letter on her laptop and asked her to post it from a village post box over forty miles away from where I lived where there were no cameras. They were ridiculous measures, I know, but total paranoia had set in. My friend, the absolute angel that she is, followed my instructions and within a week of posting it there were changes. Mathew and Barry had completely stopped. They stopped bullying, belittling, taking drugs at work and they stopped the grooming. They completely stopped giving their staff a hard time. They'd gone from being the biggest egotistical gobshites I'd ever met to quiet almost invisible librarians hiding behind their computer screens in the office overnight. Had my letter worked? I hoped it had prompted urgent action from the company, it must have. No one could ignore the threat of the police being called into their business, but the truth is I would never know for sure if the letter had any impact. During those few days between sending the letter and the company receiving it Rebecca was sectioned under the mental health act and put into hospital because her drug addiction had become out of control and her mental health had deteriorated to a point of frequent, hysterical outbursts being displayed in the warehouse. Had HR questioned them over the accusations in the letter? Or had Rebecca's sectioning frightened them into retreat and silence? I could never find out without revealing I was involved in the letter. All I know is that poor girl suffered for months at the hands of two people supposed to be there to develop and protect her in a workplace. She returned to work a couple of months later. She was questioned by HR about the accusations in the letter but denied everything and she never spoke openly about her experiences again. She got on with her job heavily medicated and switched off from her trauma. Mathew and Barry showed just how concerned they were about their "special" friend that they had spent so much time with and never spoke to her or went near her again. In fact, the grooming and hitting on girls never came back and they suddenly became a lot more discreet about their drug taking. Rebecca relapsed after a few months back from rehab, she was caught taking pills at work and was dismissed immediately, which must have been a huge relief for the two people I will forever hold responsible for her downfall.

I really believed no price could be found for my principles, but after these events I found that level and it was a very low one, no pay offs or cheques to buy my silence or inaction, I just got to keep a low-end job that I no longer liked for basic wages. When the reality of what I let happen hit me I was overcome by guilt which then evolved into becoming very bitter towards my job. I continued to work well and uphold my own standards purely because I didn't want them to have an impact on my own ethics, but I no longer possessed the patience to handle their methods lightly. I became a lot more confrontational and argumentative towards the leaders every time they tried to impose something new, which didn't go down well at all.

So going back to the first chapter, that morning, when Barry tried to grill me for being late after he had briefed out the holiday changes and the coffee limitations, I snapped back at him. He had become an absolute low life and I couldn't stand listening to him any longer. I'd never taken him seriously as a person, but by that point every time he spoke, I instantly felt angry at the thought of having to take instructions or orders from such a horrible little groomer. So I answered back every time and he didn't know how to handle it. He got used to dealing with weak people, so my behaviour then eventually led to me being a target for the management, to be squeezed from the business by his pressure, but it didn't work.

He'd come to the line each day after I began snapping at him with a big grin on his face and he would give me an order list of what he wanted built that day which was always way over my expected target. When I pointed this out to him, he'd say, "Well that's what I need, so it's going to be an awkward situation if it's not all there by the end of the day!"

"Awkward for you, Barry, you can't make me go over the targets."

"I can just move the targets up!"

"Not without a just cause, you have to consult the engineers as it could affect the quality of the build, even I know that much."

"We'll just see, won't we?"

Empty threats, that's all it was. They couldn't move the targets to my line up again unless they could prove they'd found a way to save time in the production process which was tricky for my line because they knew I'd call them out as liars if they tried to bodge the numbers like they did the others. I'd make too much noise about it and draw attention to their methods. So after a few weeks of his orders not being met but my targets still being covered he was starting to look bad in the eyes of Rochelle as orders were being missed and contracts were getting close to being lost, so he made the decision to move me over to Mathew's line. This move did three things. One, it freed up the line I was on, to put saps on there who he could manipulate and intimidate; two, he could falsify the improvement forms without ever being challenged in order to put the targets up; and three, it got his last spirited worker out of his hair and into Mathew's. Mathew had the biggest reputation among the leaders for getting the "problems" out of the business and relished the idea of getting rid of me because I was one of the few left, that stood up for myself.

• During my transfer they removed all teas and coffees completely. Staff were allowed to get drinks in their short break times only

• Hot food provided by the canteen for sale at break times was removed from the warehouse

• Warehouse reps who could previously raise concerns above Rochelle on behalf of the workers were told all questions had to be vetted by Rochelle before they were taken to meetings. She removed all questions that put her in an unfavourable light

• Training rates and overtime rates were cut by half

• All return-to-work interviews were to be filled out and signed by ourselves in our own ten-minute break times on the computer as well as holiday requests

• Appraisals and reviews had to be filled out in our own

time and although not compulsory on paper, we were forced to do it. Any that didn't put the leaders in a favourable light were destroyed or not submitted for file.

• Employee reviews were used as an opportunity to smear the character of strong workers on record so that their careers wouldn't be able to advance any further at the company. Any complaints you gave about your review were never upheld.

• They began doing their compulsory fire drills right in the middle of the factory's dinner break so that the drill never interfered with production and the time was never given back.

• When serious accidents occurred, they would predate/forge training sheets for that particular area to make it look as though the operator was at fault and not the company for its lack of training. Anyone who refused to sign the pre dated sheet was threatened with immediate dismissal.

• All doctor, dentist and hospital appointments had to be taken as holiday or unpaid leave and each appointment had to be booked onto the computer in our own break time.

Mathew wasted no time in hounding me. He knew he never had to be right in what he did or said, he just had to be loud and confrontational. One of his methods was to come around psyched and pumped up ready to have a slanging match and catch you completely off guard. So, you could be stood there quietly going about your job, then all of a sudden, a really loud voice would shout out from right behind you, making you jump and putting you immediately on the back foot as a tirade of abuse and criticisms come your way. Always loud enough to draw the attention of the whole team, make them stop what they were doing and watch him dress you down in public. It was his favourite management technique and it was always embarrassing and humiliating whether you were watching or the one it was aimed at. He'd talk too loud and too fast at you, so it was almost impossible for you to ready a reply to it but on the odd occasion you were quick enough to address his rant he'd come straight back at you with another one. Example, my first day on his line I was being trained to build on the first stage. The trainer had been telling me all that morning what a great job I was doing and remarked how quick I was picking everything up, stating what I'd learned in one morning could take some operators three days to grasp, so I knew my progress was going well. Mathew then comes right up behind me while I'm concentrating, bangs a tool down on the metal counter and shouts right in my ear, "What sort of numbers are those!", pointing to the target computer screen that sat above the line, "the whole line is falling behind right now because they're waiting on you to send the work down. You need to pick this up, it's not good enough."

"But I'm in training."

"You're what?" The tools around me shut off as the other operators began to tune into the show.

"I'm in training, there's not supposed to be any pressure on me while I'm working, until I'm signed off, we're only two behind on the board and nobody is waiting for work."

"THIS IS MY LINE! And I run it to a different standard to everyone else. I expect good numbers whether someone's training or not!"

"But how can I..."

"Do you know how many staff I've let go of on this line because they weren't fast enough? And some of them were quicker than you! You're not on the easy lines any more, so you're gonna have to pick it up or there are going to be consequences!" He walked off straight away after not allowing me to get another word in. It was absolute bollocks and fucking infuriating. There was nothing wrong with my work rate at all, this was all to apply pressure. This went on every single day without fail and it was all being aimed at me. Mathew was determined to keep his promise in breaking me, so he picked holes in everything I did. If I was being trained on a new stage, it wasn't good enough. If I made a mistake or a small error, even if I was still in training, he grilled me in front of everyone, which never happened to anyone else. If I went to get water, he accused me of being off the line too long and slowing everyone up when the whole thing took less than a minute. He'd also generalise by saying things like you're always getting water and always chatting away instead of working. I wasn't always doing anything! It was all bullshit that couldn't be proved one way or the other. What was important, of course, was that the pressure stuck and after a time, despite my best efforts to shrug it off, it was having an effect. As strong as I was mentally these daily confrontations began to wear me down, and after a couple of months, I actually began to feel anxious and frightened about going to work. I didn't realise just how on edge I'd become until the first day Mathew took a holiday and I felt a huge and overwhelming relief that he wouldn't be showing up behind me that day. I was upset at myself once more for tolerating his and the company's crap. I desperately wanted to leave but anxiety was coursing through every one of my veins and I was too frightened to see what was out there beyond my current employment. My confidence had truly been knocked by weeks and months of put downs and constantly being told I wasn't good enough and I was lucky to have a job there. Feeling every day that I was being pushed out either by quitting or being forced into a series of false accusations I signed up to a workers' union. The union couldn't enter the workplace, but I knew they could provide legal advice and I'd also have their representation if it got to the point where I was dismissed unfairly. I also began writing down the confrontations I had with Mathew. Times, dates, places, who was there and what was said onto little notes fresh after the incident with as much detail as possible. His behaviour continued for roughly another month, although he did back off for a little bit when work was informed about my membership by the union, but it didn't last long. He was back ranting and making nasty little comments within a week or two and after a couple of months it all came to a head.

The whole line, about eight of us were taken into the office by Mathew about ten o'clock one morning for an "emergency" meeting, but we all knew what this actually meant. Rochelle had obviously screamed at Mathew about his line underperforming and he was going to take it all out on us. The idea of these meetings was to get to the bottom of why there had been any performance issues and find ways to put things right and back on track, a problem-solving exercise, but it never went in that direction because the line leaders used it as an opportunity to have a go at the whole team, rip them apart, then ask them why it was happening. When people previously put their hands up in these meetings with suggestions as to why things weren't ideal like "the testing machine is being slow", it was always met with an arsy, negative reply, "I think you'll find that tester is working fine!" even if it wasn't, so they learned there was never any point in saying anything. It always got batted down, no matter how relevant or serious the issue was; no one put their hands up any more. The whole process had become an awkward encounter between leaders and staff where the leaders would rant, and we'd all sit there in silence when they demanded ways for improvement. The silence would last until we were dismissed from the meeting room and absolutely nothing was achieved.

This particular morning Mathew looked enraged. Every inch of his wide and fat face was bright red. He was breathing heavily and pumped full of adrenaline. Rochelle must have given him a right going over because he'd come from her office before calling the meeting and he was really mad. Right from the start he was yelling out at the top of his voice effing and blinding, telling everyone their attitudes were appalling and we needed to sort them out or start looking for another job. He accused us of hanging around on the line and chatting rather than working. This was most likely from Rochelle seeing us stood still in the twenty seconds she observed us and not seeing the maintenance team repairing our line, which took all of about two minutes, but that fact didn't matter to either of them, can't let the truth get in the way of a twenty-second window! So there was no point in explaining it. They'd made up their minds and there's no convincing them of the truth once they did. He ranted on about how we weren't good enough, everybody, especially Rochelle was extremely disappointed in our performances and Jimmy would be keeping a closer eye on our line from that moment. Throughout the whole meeting Mathew lost almost complete control of his emotions, foaming and spitting as he shouted and put us down. No one said a word back to it.

"Get out! And pick the fucking numbers up or you're

going!" and as I began to walk past him to leave, "Could you stay behind please? I'd like to have a word with you in private."

"This doesn't sound good. Do I need to bring a witness in for this 'chat'?"

"If you feel you need one!" Like that little spectacle wasn't enough I was going to get my own personal performance from him. The rest of my team had already vacated so I walked out of the office and asked the first person I could see if they could be a witness for "our chat". The poor sod was a lovely twenty-one-year-old lad called Luke who kept his head down at work and tried to avoid trouble at all costs. You could tell by his face he'd wished I'd asked anyone else other than him but, fair play to him, there were no objections, he put his tools down and followed me back into the office. As we walked in Mathew slammed the door shut behind us, then as calm as he could muster, he said, "take a seat" like he was stupidly trying to play good cop and bad cop at the same time. Luke sat down in a chair in the corner close to the door. Mathew and I sat opposite each other with a small, circular desk between us in the middle of the tiny office. Mathew sat forward in the chair, elbows on the desk and turned up to full volume again.

"Right, it's been spotted by management that you've been going to the toilet too many times and when you are going, you're spending too much time in there! It's affecting your work! Every time I've come over to the line, you're not there! And the work is piling up on your stage! It's not good enough and it stops now! I'm going to be recording your visits from now on and if it's deemed too much again, I will be taking it further. Do I make myself clear?"

I was so shocked by the whole thing that I actually laughed back at him reservedly and nervously. What the fuck was going on? It was so ridiculous I was waiting for someone to explain that this whole thing was some sort of crap prank, stood in the next room waiting to reveal the whole scenario was a joke that wasn't very funny, but he was deadly serious. There was absolutely nothing wrong with what I was doing and there was absolutely nothing wrong with my toilet breaks. I went the same number of times for the same amount of time as everyone else; this whole conversation/rant was insane. I had no doubt that this was all Rochelle's doing, though. She had probably seen me going to the toilet once that morning, then complained and generalised to Mathew that she's always seeing me go and allowed Mathew to make up the rest. That's your job is it, Rochelle, a lying and inaccurate toilet monitor! You sad fucking joke of a manager. I reached the point in that meeting where I felt so fed up with feeling anxious because of these people, every minute of every day being on edge. I finally let go of it and said to myself, sod it, what have I really got to lose? And I also knew this time he couldn't run away from the confrontation, so I began picking apart his stupid little argument.

"Who's concerned about my toilet breaks?"

"Myself and management, and that's all you need to know."

"Okay, so they have anonymity, so exactly how long is too long to use the toilet?"

"Long enough to be noticed by management."

"That's not really an answer, is it, Mathew?"

"Well, it is, if they've deemed it too much and too long, then you must be going too much and too long."

"How many times is too often, Mathew? Is there a specific number?"

"Enough when it's noticed by management!"

"That's not a number, is it, mate? That means you could pick any number you want to and tell me it's too often."

"Look, at the end of the day, every time I've come over to the line you're not there. The work is stacked up on your stage, and no one seems to know where you are!"

"That's not true, though, is it? I know it's not."

"Are you calling me a liar?"

"No, I'm saying you're mistaken, When's the last time you came over to the line and found the work built up on my stage?"

"This morning! I came over and you were nowhere to be seen and no one could work because it was all piled up on your stage!"

"What time was that, then?"

"This morning."

"Well, can you be more specific? Because I'm more than happy to go and ask the team to see if they can recall when the work was all piled up on me."

"You don't need to because I saw it."

"I'm going to ask them anyway because I know you're wrong about this, plus the warehouse has CCTV. I'm pretty sure that would help prove no work had built up in my area."

He absolutely hated being boxed in there with me, unable to walk away from his own bullshit. He was unravelling.

"Look, at the end of the day your behaviour and your attitude simply isn't good enough, and your toilet breaks will now be monitored and if it's deemed too much, this issue will be escalated."

"You can't do that, especially when you can't justify why."

"Well, I just have, and I can, if you don't like it, you're more than welcome to go and discuss this with Rochelle!"

"I think I will but not until I have taken advice from my union."

Straight away he gave me this crazed laugh from across the table. "Good luck! Unions aren't recognised here, mate."

"That doesn't mean I can't get legal advice from them, Mathew, that is my right, and there's nothing you can do legally to prevent me. Am I able to go and speak to them now?"

"No, you can't, you can wait until your lunch break for personal phone calls, and in the meantime, I'll go and inform Rochelle you would like to discuss this further with her."

"Well, tell her I'm only going to speak to her after I have spoken to someone from my union, which will now be after lunch."

He laughed at me once more as he stood up to conclude the meeting. "You're wasting your time, mate."

He kicked his chair back across the room and stormed out.

# Chapter Nine

## The Grievance

That meeting was the final straw for me. His sheer arrogance and his really aggressive behaviour, was just too much. This wasn't a one off either. He thought speaking to me in such a disgusting way was totally acceptable and justified because he showed absolutely no remorse post meeting. In fact, he went straight into another meeting with another member of staff and did exactly the same thing to them. I decided I would wait until he arranged the meeting with Rochelle that afternoon and I would make it clear to her that not only was his anger and attitude unprofessional, it was disgusting and unacceptable and I would be pressing for formal action to be taken against his conduct. I didn't speak to my union at lunch as I'd threatened. Instead, I phoned the twenty-four-hour legal service that's provided by my union membership to seek advice on his monitoring of my toilet breaks and the fact he was consistently treating me in such a poor way. The lady on the legal team I spoke to was very polite and professional; unfortunately, she couldn't give me any news that brought relief from the severe anger and anxiety I was experiencing. She said, "Although what he's doing is highly immoral, technically speaking it's not illegal, therefore it would be very unlikely any action could be taken against him or the company for it." Great! The ace up my sleeve turned out to be the joker of the pack; the union wouldn't be able to help me with this. Not only that but after telling him I'd be speaking to my union and seeing his smug face change suddenly to one of uncertainty I was going to enter that meeting with Rochelle with my tail between my legs knowing nothing could be done about it. Further embarrassment could also arise if they asked about the outcome of my conversation with them. My anger was quickly replaced with nervousness. I felt sick. My whole body turned clammy. I couldn't face a single mouthful of my lunch. This place where I'd come to earn an honest but crappy wage and keep my head down had become an extremely hostile environment where I'm having to defend myself constantly and unnecessarily and there was a load more to come. It was escalating, more fighting, more confrontation, more anxiety and stress.

I sat in my car staring at my lunch and my coffee cup contemplating starting the engine, pulling out of the premises and never looking back, but the more I examined the options in that decision the more I realised it was equally as daunting and equally as stressful as staying. Where could I go? What could I do after this place? I was a creaking, overweight thirty-one-year-old with bad joints, tight lungs and no qualifications. I threw the last years of my youth into this place, hoping it would be a decent place to settle.

I could go to all the job agencies in town and sign on again! But then I'd have to hope they could string me together a full week's work since the recession had hit, and live from day to day. The only big companies left in town that were taking on temp to perm contracts had reputations even worse than my place for the way they treated staff and paid even less too! I felt trapped as there was no real power in my choice. I stayed sitting in my car and felt the tears began to stream down my face, my break was almost up, and I was going to go back in and take more and I couldn't handle it mentally. The way they treated people and got away with it, time and time again, wasn't right. Mathew was a bully, plain and simple, and with threatening and intimidation his only managing tools. I was in no doubt that he'd been picked by Rochelle on those assets alone, but he should have been nowhere near that position. Someone had to stand up to him; I just didn't want it to be me.

I returned reluctantly to my workstation after break, waiting to be summoned to Rochelle's lair. My mind was in overdrive trying to anticipate every angle they could come after me. Did I need another witness? Definitely. Was I now going to be facing two of them with the same objective to shame, embarrass and belittle me without just cause and over such a personal subject? Would she be nasty and hostile too? What could she threaten me with? Did she have the power or the authority to dismiss me over this? Be suspended? I was playing out the various questions and scenarios in my head. It was the only way I could feel I had any chance and control over this situation. I was riddled with anxiety and distraction and my work was suffering. I began to make loads of mistakes on the line, little concentration was lent to what was in front of me, only building up more stress and tension as I felt as though they would have even more ammunition to fire at me.

Time was dragging too; it seemed like the longest afternoon of my life. I couldn't look forward to checking out and going home like normal because I knew something uncomfortable was going to happen between then and finish time. When it got to half past three that afternoon it all began to change. I had been back at work a couple of hours at that point and no one had approached me. Mathew was avoiding my area completely and Rochelle and Jimmy were nowhere to be seen. What the hell was happening? This life-threatening issue that I had created for them through imaginary toilet breaks that warranted shouting and bawling at me until he was red in the face and had to be escalated with the uppermost urgency had suddenly been forgotten about.

At four o'clock I finally saw Mathew waddle up the mezzanine steps to her office and I thought then it was beginning. He came back out after about twenty minutes, obviously giving his watered-down and twisted version of events. I thought he was coming down to summon me to her office, but he didn't! And ten minutes later she came out of her office with her handbag, laptop under arm and her coat on, leaving early as she always did to beat the post-work traffic. They obviously didn't want to deal with it there and then, they were going to leave me to sweat and worry about it overnight while they built a solid attack to launch at me the next day.

I never take my work home with me. One of the only perks left of my job is when I clock out, I get to leave all my work problems at the clocking-in machine. On this occasion I couldn't. My composure had eroded, and I was completely rattled by the day's events. I returned home and explained everything to my mum and girlfriend. Years of witnessing unfair dismissals, cutting off those who suddenly needed a little support from the company they gave so much to, the accidents that were covered up, the months of backhanded comments, awkward and public confrontations about my development, the perks being stripped away from us at the bottom, the questioning of my toilet breaks, the meeting that took place that day and the legal technicalities that worked in their favour, everything poured out of me. My mum, not one to mince her words, told me that they were "fucking out of order!" And "he can't get away with that!" My girlfriend was just as shocked. She couldn't believe people could be pulled up on toilet breaks and management could use this loophole to bully employees at will and not be answerable to anyone about it. She's an office worker and held various office roles over her working life including a job in human resources for a major bank for a number of years and had never heard of anything like this before.

Their reaction instantly gave me a sense of comfort. I wasn't going mad! This behaviour wasn't right, it wasn't acceptable, but what should I do now? I could hope they took the threat of contacting my union as a sign they were vulnerable in areas of the law they hadn't thought of and they would want this to go away quickly and quietly and bother me no further, and to be honest, I wanted this option myself, I wasn't cut out for this sort of stuff. I could get called up to Rochelle's office, not put up any sort of a fight, take the unnecessary ear bashing and the put downs, just go back to my workstation and return to a quiet existence trying carefully from that moment forward not to tread on anyone's toes again, but that wouldn't work long term. Once a bully is confident you are weak it could become easier to pressure you and humiliate you in the future because they know there are no repercussions from their actions.

The only option I truly had was to take it to them, go on the offensive in some way. I had to stand my ground with him and Rochelle because at the very least he'd know not to try anything else like this with me in the future because it would be more hassle than it was worth.

I decided if Rochelle was going to spend another day avoiding me, whether it was to play mind games or hope the issue would simply go away, I would take the initiative and go and see her. I was going to make it clear I wasn't going to tolerate any of their bullshit.

I went to work the next day and discovered Mathew wasn't there, he was on holiday, which instantly took some pressure off me; there wouldn't be any confrontations from him to contend with first thing or more shitty comments throughout the day. It meant I only had to deal with Rochelle and knowing I couldn't be outnumbered I felt a little more confident. I decided I would give her until lunchtime to come to me and address this "important" issue and if she didn't, I would go to her after lunch and talk it out. It got to lunch, and no one came, fine, their avoidance at that point was only filling me with a determination anyway. After my lunch break, I went straight to her office and she wasn't there. I knew Jimmy was also away on holiday, so I went to the next person in charge, which was Steven. "All right, mate, I'm looking for Rochelle. Have you seen her?"

"She was this morning but decided to take half a day in lieu."

"Really, she been putting in the hours then?" asking sarcastically, knowing she hadn't and was just fudging the hours to go and bonk her new fella.

"Ha! Yeah, right, you'll be lucky if she hits thirty hours a week, mate, what's up?"

"Can we go somewhere private, mate?"

Steve took me into the production office, and I told him everything that had happened from the beginning of my time working under Mathew. First thing that he suggested was that I sat down with himself and Mathew and we discussed everything, a mediation. I replied that I felt we're now past this stage as I'd already spoken with Jimmy regarding Mathew and it just accelerated Mathew's bad behaviour after. I also knew he (Mathew) was the sort of spineless cretin that would deny absolutely everything despite there being a witness present and make any encounter as difficult, and as stressful as possible. He would twist and turn anything to provoke and cause a reaction from me. This was the world he lived in and thrived on; he was totally comfortable lying to people's faces.

I knew that if I was to be taken seriously, composure must be maintained at all times, remove any emotions I may have about the events and stick to the facts; a meeting with him had the potential to get a reaction that wouldn't work in my favour.

Credit to Steven, he listened to everything I'd said intently and then offered some more options. "Well, you can speak to Rochelle when she comes in on Monday? Or the other thing you can do is raise a formal grievance against Mathew and hand it in to HR."

As nice and professional as Steven had been for that fifteen minutes, I left that meeting feeling I had a mountain to climb. Three years I'd been there and with all the dodgy, near the mark and illegal incidents I'd witnessed in all that time not once did I ever see human resources become involved. In fact, the only time I ever saw the HR manager was when she was getting coffee with Rochelle or going to lunch with the directors. She was in her mid-twenties, quite a good-looking woman and the only other thing I'd observed about her was that she was more concerned with her appearance and making the right impression on the right people than she was with actually doing her job and remaining impartial. I never bore her a grudge for that. She reminded me that fairness could be bought up; it had a price. She had bills to pay and a job to secure in a department where there were a hundred people ready to step into her shoes should she fail or let the company down, and to her that came before being impartial. Despite my reservations about the HR manager, a grievance seemed like the only way in which this issue couldn't be completely swept under the carpet. It would be my only chance of making them back off.

I'd booked some holiday months before this incident for the week after it, so I had some time on my side to construct a solid grievance. I decided I was going to handle this on my own and not to contact or inform my union about this for three reasons. Firstly, I had been reminded by nearly every member of management on so many occasions before that the company did not and would not recognise a union in their workplace despite my fully paid-up membership and they'd refuse them in at any opportunity they could, they would let them in as much as the laws dictated but no more. Forcing the issue of union rights into the grievance could potentially cause further problems and the reality is people's backs go up when they're suddenly out of their comfort zones or they drag their heels when they're obligated to face something they don't want to. I needed the wall of human resources to be kept as low as possible at all times to build a relationship with anyone in that department who could sympathise with my position and help me from within the company.

The second reason is on the surface of things, it could be seen as too aggressive, too rash. I was smart/lucky enough to have joined my union a good couple of months before all this kicked off, so there was nothing to stop them assisting me, but how it could be perceived was important. I joined a union and roughly a couple of months later I'm getting them involved with all their resources into the company's business. It could look as though this whole thing was a pre-planned assault on the company rather than just a coincidental requirement. I had to leave the union out of it, I had to appear fair and open to resolution despite my desire to nail Mathew's fat ass to the walls of the warehouse.

The third reason is that I wanted to take on this challenge myself, sort of, by myself, I mean, with the help of my family and friends but on my own with no legal assistance. I understood from the moment I was pulled into that office this could well be the beginning of something. To put pressure on me to leave like they did all the others since I started. I had to understand more about my employment rights, I had to understand more about what they could and couldn't get away with because this was going to carry on until I quit and gave up or got smart and fought back.

I clocked out Friday afternoon, originally believing my well-deserved and long overdue break from work would begin straight after. It was supposed to be a week filled with coastal walks and country pubs. Instead, it had been replaced with a big and job-altering challenge that if I got right would put a pin prick into the heart of their regime and hopefully make some people in higher places (owner level) start asking questions about why such tyrannical management had been allowed for so long in a business that prided itself on being a family. One false move on my part and they'd pounce like wild animals on any flaw or fault in my grievance, to make an example of me and deter anyone else from standing up for themselves in the future.

I called my mum and girlfriend and asked them to meet me at home. I explained what was happening and we got right to work. We began by dragging out every note that I had made about every significant incident that had taken place at work over the last few months to begin building a strong case.

Any note or incident that was missing any information at all was removed from the case. They would be nothing but chinks in the armour; any questions put to me that I couldn't answer would look weak and would affect the outcome. I had to be confident that every piece of information that went in there could be backed up with witnesses, exact times and dates of confrontations that could all be verified by the twenty-four-hour CCTV in the warehouse if it came to it. Once the notes were sorted, we began constructing the grievance, researching and pulling up similar cases online and looking at how they were constructed and what the outcomes were and what laws were actually being broken.

By Wednesday after a lot of hard work from all three of us my statement was ready. Four watertight incidents typed up on the laptop, courtesy of Mum and printed off at my girlfriend's workplace with a covering letter to HR stating I'd like to raise a formal grievance. Keeping a copy for file at home, I began memorising all nine pages of it, every line absorbed, prepared for any question or variable they could throw at me. If I failed, there would be no more hope for me staying there, Mathew would feel like he had got a win and was untouchable. It had to succeed.

Thursday afternoon my girlfriend finished work early and picked me up from my house. She presented me with the finished document. I read it all through one last time, double checking every word, every sentence to make sure there were no mistakes. When I finished, I placed it all inside a pre-addressed envelope, licked and sealed it shut. She looked at me with her big, brown and beautiful eyes and asked me one last time, "Are you sure this is what you want to do? I'll help you find another job. You don't have to go through with this."

By this point not doing anything was worse than trying and failing and I could always find another job after when it went tits up! "It's what I want." She started the engine and pulled away.

When we arrived, I got out of the car and went in alone. But rather than walk through the main doors and turn right to go on to the HR department I turned left and headed for the warehouse. I didn't have to do this, of course, but I knew Jimmy was back at work and in his office and I wanted to know if he was up to date on everything that happened while he was off and this wasn't for my or his benefit at all. I wanted Mathew to see me in there talking to the supervisors, holding a full envelope in my hand looking smart, confident and in control. It instantly had the desired effect, because as I spoke to Jimmy, I could see Mathew in the edge of my vision peering over several times while he was supposed to be in conversation with another member of staff. His eyes widened and the rolls of fat from under his grotty chin bunched up every time he turned his eyes towards me. Jimmy confirmed he'd been briefed by Steven and I left straight away, head up, shoulders slightly back and trying my best to maintain the image of absolute control while he fell apart in curiosity and I hoped, a slight anxiety. Mathew knew at that moment it was going to be escalated and all he could do was stand there and wait for the venom of my tiny bite to slowly course through his veins. He couldn't prove I'd done that on purpose; all he could do was watch me walk off with trouble for him in my hands. He was utterly powerless to do anything, finally, he had a taste of his own medicine and it felt good to be holding the spoon that fed it.

I walked past reception and into the office area, which is always awkward because the staff there never looked comfortable with warehouse operators going in there, you'd think from the way they looked at us we were from another planet or something, but we went in there often enough to remind them that we were indeed human too and not primitive beings there to keep the money flowing in for their comfortable existences. They really believed they were a cut above their warehouse counterparts, but they weren't paid any more than us. I walked past all the admin staff and straight over to the HR office. I was in battle mode ready to front up against this corrupt and bought HR manager and show her what I was made of. I knocked on the already partly open door and looked into the room to discover that the HR manager wasn't there. There was another lady in there, though, sitting at the smaller of the two cheap, mass produced, DIY assembled chipboard desks. She was average in height, well into her fifties, long blonde hair that if unravelled from her bun would reach right down near her bottom and a hardened, wrinkled and aged face that screamed at me that she must be puffing forty a day minimum.

She was very politely and softly spoken. "Hi, I'm Tanya, can I help you?"

Quickly calming myself down from confrontation mode I replied, "Hi, yes, I'm looking for the HR manager, is she around at all?"

"She's in a meeting at the moment, I'm afraid, but I'm also in HR and work directly under her, is there something I can help with?"

I explained why I was there and handed over the letter. "You didn't have to hand this in immediately, you could have waited until you had returned from your holiday."

"Yeah, I know, but I didn't want it hanging over my head." (Just didn't trust any of them.)

"Well, it's here now, it's done, so please don't let this spoil the rest of your break." She appeared to be genuine and sincere, but I wasn't going to be manipulated by the first sign of kindness. For all I knew she could be exactly like her boss underneath, but she was polite to me and deserved nothing less in return. "We'll begin the investigation while you're away and hopefully we'll have some findings when you come back."

"Thanks very much, it was nice meeting you."

"Now go! Get out of here and don't think on it."

A surprisingly positive and pleasant encounter, totally different from my expectations. I left the office riding on a high. I did as I was told, I enjoyed my last few days down by the coast and I didn't give any of it another thought.

Monday morning arrived and a rare phenomenon had taken place in my bedroom... I'd beaten the alarm clock. I hadn't done that for years. It was because I was extremely nervous about my return to work. Not knowing what fate awaited me. Would I be met with fairness? Open-mindedness or aggression? It was too late to pull out of it all, it was about living with the consequences of my decision.

I got to work, clocked in and assembled at my morning brief as normal expecting to be called away by HR at any moment as surely they weren't going to allow me to continue working, with somebody I had made such strong allegations against? There was nothing, no call, no one from HR coming in to whisk me away, no note, nothing. Mathew appeared from his standing workstation looking slightly more serious than normal, read out the team brief and told us to go to our workstations.

I was expecting some sort of drama to unfold in the brief, some display of emotion or nastiness from him but again there was nothing. He didn't even threaten anyone or remind us of our rules like normal. I went to my area feeling a little flat, to be honest. By three o'clock at the last break still nothing had developed, so I approached Jimmy at his desk. "Hello, mate, I was wondering if there had been any investigation regarding my grievance since I've been away? I'm just after any updates really."

"Yeah, of course," he replied, shuffling papers at his desk, making little eye contact and pretending to look busy. "I've been briefed that an investigation is to be carried out by myself as I'm impartial to the grievance and as soon as I'm given an authorisation email from Tanya to begin I will. Unfortunately, she's on holiday this week, so I probably won't receive the email until she's back next week. I can't begin until then."

"Okay, mate, cheers, what happens in the meantime?"

"What do you mean?"

"I put in my letter I'd like to be moved from Mathew's area to avoid any awkwardness and avoid any further confrontations with him."

"Has there been any this morning?"

"No, but that doesn't mean it won't happen in the future if we're kept together in the same team."

"If there's any problems, come and see me and I will deal

with it, but for now we have to keep you there for the need of the business, to move you around would cause staffing problems."

"Right, okay, thanks for your time, Jimmy, I'll check in with you next week then, see if the email has come through."

"No worries."

What a load of crap, was the first thought I had when I left his workstation. The suck up of a HR manager was there in the building, I'd seen her myself that morning following Rochelle around like an attention-seeking puppy getting a coffee together and the letter was formally addressed to her. Are you telling me as a manager she couldn't give the authorisation to begin the investigation? Of course, she could, they were biding time. And what a load of bull from Jimmy too about not being moved away from Mathew because of staffing problems. I knew the training matrix as well as he did. I could have done a straight swap with at least three other members of staff as they were trained on my lines and I was trained on theirs without any impact on the skill levels. It's almost as if they wanted me to stay in that environment, in close proximity with him. Maybe I'd snap, lose my temper, become irrational or do something to discredit myself or walk out and make their investigation a whole lot easier. I didn't complain or argue despite my fears as it would seem aggressive and forceful. I believed this was their way of trying to push me early on to find faults in my behaviour. As long as I continued to play by their rules, they weren't going to find any.

I let six working days pass by, working under that lump of dough who by that point was giving me the awkward silent treatment in front of everybody. Despite my worries I took it as nothing but a good sign; after all a person of morals and standing on the right side of the law and reason would stand their ground or act with dignity and have nothing to fear. The fact he was blatantly ignoring me only confirmed what a sad little bully he was. He had no response of any decency or decorum. I was also being kept in the dark by those that were supposed to be carrying out the investigation too! While they conjured up possible arguments to the truth and I had to bear this all-in silence, not being able to talk to another soul about it as instructed by HR and Jimmy, my grievance had to be kept private and confidential. It didn't seem fair at all, talking to someone about it would have released so much pressure but the rules are the rules. If Mathew was totally innocent of my accusations and I had spent weeks tarnishing his name and reputation, that wouldn't be fair. He wasn't, of course, but the rules are there to serve the interests of all parties despite my desires to confide.

On Tuesday afternoon I began looking for Jimmy and he was nowhere to be seen. I asked colleagues working close to his desk if they'd seen him, but no one had all day. I then asked Steve. "Not sure where he is, mate, he might be on a course today."

"Of course, he is."

"Yep, he's away in Salisbury all this week, mate, he won't be in until next week," he replied as he continued to scroll through the communal diary screen on his computer.

"You might catch him near the end of the day as I'm pretty sure he's gotta come in and collect some course notes for tomorrow but you'll be lucky if you catch him, technically he's not down as being here for the day."

"Okay, Steve, cheers, if you do catch him, can you tell him I'm looking for him?"

He was stalling for time once more. I was sure of it. Being old friends with Steve I knew the company booked these courses weeks in advance because they're done externally, and they needed to confirm the bookings with the companies that held them.

I was angry, but once more I couldn't show it. It's exactly what they wanted for their report. I decided to wait behind after finishing time to see if he turned up and I could catch him off guard. He wouldn't expect me to be hanging around. I got myself a cup of coffee and sat in the canteen and waited. Less than ten minutes later he slithered into the warehouse when he thought no one else was around for a hassle-free retrieval of his folder, but I went and surprised him at his desk.

You'd have thought I was wearing a Halloween mask the way he jumped out of his skin at my presence.

"Oh, hello, mate, you, all right?" instantly breaking eye contact yet again as soon as he could, his brain running on overdrive trying to compose himself after his surprise, but to little success.

"I suppose you want to talk to me about your grievance?" Rummaging around his desk he could not have made it any more obvious this was the last conversation he wanted to be having before ending his working day, and this was supposed to be my go-to guy. I said nothing in reply. I let a few agonising seconds pass by just looking at him until he was almost forced into filling the silence once more. "Well, I've been put on this course last minute, mate, and it's going to run all week, so I won't be able to begin my investigation until I finish the course unfortunately. As you can imagine I'm now really snowed under as I have to do this course as well as my normal duties." Normal duties? What normal duties were they exactly? Unless he meant being topped up on the hair gel he used excessively and breath mints he used to keep Rochelle's butthole smelling like a pack of chewing gum as he followed her around.

"I see, that's not very fair on you is it, mate? You'd have thought they would have given you some notice to prepare for it rather than just drop you in it last minute."

"Yeah, exactly, very annoying, mate."

"Perhaps next time you should refuse to go on such short notice particularly when you have a huge stack of work to do now in your normal role."

"Yeah, but what can you do! I've got to get these courses done as part of my development."

"Well, even more reason to give you as much time as possible to prepare, mate."

I was enjoying watching him squirm. His lying was almost as bad as his Hitler youth style haircut that was coming back into fashion but belonged on a lad ten years younger than him.

"So I won't be able to begin your investigation until next week I'm afraid, mate, I'm sorry, that's just the way it is."

"No worries, Jimmy, it's clear you're very busy. I can wait until next week but as long as you promise me that it will definitely be dealt with next week."

"Definitely, one hundred percent, next week won't be a problem at all."

"That's great, thanks, Jimmy, I hope the rest of your course goes well and I will check in with you next week then, see you later."

The conversation finished just in time to see Tom walk past and watch Jimmy instantly go into hyper creep mode and start complimenting the short arse on his new shoes. Where was the nearest bucket?

I left the whole thing alone until the Thursday after because he'd have finished his "last minute, I can't believe it, it was such a shock and complete surprise to me, but really wasn't course" and gave him a few days back at work to catch up with his non-work, so he was left with no excuses to put to me.

"Jimmy, you got a sec, mate? Could we talk in private?"

"Not right now, to be honest with you, mate, I have a meeting to attend to in ten minutes. Go back to your line and I'll come and get you for a chat as soon as the meeting has finished."

"No worries," was my reply despite the fact the way he spoke to me almost seemed arsy and dismissive, the audacity of the guy! If he had done his job in the first place, I'd have no need to pester him and he wouldn't get stressed about trying to bypass it. I returned to my line and waited for his meeting to finish. It was being held in Rochelle's office and her door on the mezzanine floor was in my line of sight, so I knew exactly when his meeting ended. Forty-five minutes later I saw all the supervisors and leaders including Jimmy come out and head down the steps and it was a cringing sight to observe too. False smiles and fake laughs en masse filling the staircase at her parting attempt of wit was sickly and pathetic. You could tell from a mile off none of their reactions were genuine, their acting was just another opportunity to suck up to this unimpressive woman!

Right, give it five or ten minutes and he'll come and grab me, nope! Ninety minutes went by and still nothing, then he came to the line. He looked up and over at our work line with the office bike from purchasing, I waved to him, he looked right at me and he blanked me (bit embarrassing), what an absolute prick were the first words that jumped out of my mouth. I knew with absolute certainty at that moment that my grievance was all a bloody game to him and there was also no doubt that the creep breeder up the staircase was behind all of this. I'd spent weeks after my grievance putting up with Mathew's awkward confrontations and talking behind my back and not only were they ignoring my request to be moved, actively allowing this to continue, they hadn't even begun the investigation. It was really stressful. Everybody knew there was clearly a friction between Mathew and me because of the way he spoke to me like shit or ignored me whenever he was able to. Colleagues were turning around every time he approached me to fill up on gossip and those with enough front would approach me after he left to ask me what was going on between us. I couldn't and wouldn't say anything to them. They weren't my friends, they didn't care about me, they just wanted a good story to spread around. I spent weeks feeling isolated and like the whole world was watching and talking about me behind my back, Mathew was telling people I was a grass and a snake and that I'd dropped him in the shit, that I was two faced and a backstabber and these same people would come forward and tell me what he had said like they were doing me some sort of favour, but what could I do with the hearsay? It couldn't be proven. I just had to sit there and take it and close all conversations down by saying I'm not allowed to talk about it even though he was breaking the rules. Every day that I went to work I felt on edge like something could kick off from him at any moment. My anxiety was constantly running high. I had chest pains from the moment I woke till the moment I managed to fall asleep in the early hours of the morning. My face felt like a balloon ready to burst every minute of the day as if all the blood in my body was trying to climb up into my skull. It was unbearable, and they kept me there in that state deliberately for weeks by ignoring my request to be moved, ignoring my clear distress and ignoring my grievance.

As soon as the purchasing bike had gone, I left the line for the second time (which was forbidden, remember, I needed Mathew's permission) and went over to Jimmy's desk.

"Afternoon, Jimmy, have you got time for me now?"

He exhaled sharply and rudely in response to my presence and question, how bloody dare you, you cockroach!

"Yeah sure, why don't you go through to the back office and I'll be with you in five minutes," without hiding his next action he walked all the way along outside the office window, past me, walked back up the stairs to Rochelle's office (my manager who hadn't spoken to me yet regarding my welfare or the behaviour of her leadership staff) and held an emergency meeting with her, or to put it accurately, receive his next set of instructions on how to continue stalling with my grievance. So blatant and done with the intention of undermining me and it was bloody infuriating. He came back into the office a few minutes later with a smug look on his face and a very confident walk flowing through his body. I didn't address what had just happened; there was no proof he'd been to discuss my case, but it was obvious from his reaction that's what it was all about.

"Okay," he said, exhaling dramatically again as he sat down. "I'm assuming this is regarding your grievance?" Pressing his fingers together, leaning back on his cheap office chair like a shit villain from a low budget spy movie.

"Yes, I was wondering where we are with it. Have you begun your investigation yet?"

"No, not yet, I've been absolutely crazy busy with other priorities that have piled up because of my course last week, I'm afraid! No one was here to take over my job in my absence, so everything has stacked up on my desk and I'm trying my best to work my way through it."

"I see," replying to the crap that was gently trickling out of his face while wondering yet again what he actually did for a job in a department that practically ran itself. The reality was he could attend pointless meetings and go on courses because he didn't actually do anything, not a thing; holiday requests, staffing and welfare were taken care of by those below him at leader level. I couldn't think of a single thing he actually took care of personally other than grievances. He delegated everything to the point where he should be worried that the very existence of his job could come under question.

"So when do you think you'll be able to take a look at it, then?"

"Tell you what, let's say if I haven't taken a look at it by Wednesday next week, you can go straight to HR and tell them I've not been able to complete it for you."

"Okay, I'll come and see you Wednesday and find out where you are with it." (I'm fine by the way, thanks for asking, you back-covering weasel.)

Wednesday

"Where's Jimmy?" I asked Steve.

"He's on holiday, mate."

"You've got to be joking?"

"Nah, off all week, why? What's up?"

"Doesn't matter, cheers mate." (not allowed to talk about it)

I walk straight over to the HR office, speak to Tanya and fill her in on everything.

"Right, okay, well, that's just not acceptable, I'm so sorry, it had been given to him to carry out weeks ago and he was told it was of the highest priority, it should have been done by now."

The HR manager might have been willing to overlook it, but I felt Tanya was taking it seriously. Why would Rochelle and Jimmy be stalling contrary to the company's own policy on grievances?

"I'll speak to Jimmy as soon as he returns on Monday. Unfortunately, the investigation has been given to him officially, and we can't simply redistribute it until he's been informed or he's sent it back to us with a legitimate reason as to why he's been unable to complete it. Don't worry, I'm on it now and I'll speak to him first thing."

As soon as I got home that evening I went straight onto my laptop and starting researching HR procedures on the internet, not even sparing the time to strip naked of my grease-covered uniform to find out whether the company had been sticking to the legal protocols, and straight away in my search an article come up in HR procedures and work tribunals with the following: "an application must be made to an employment tribunal three months minus one day of the date when the event you are complaining about last happened. If your application is received after this time, the tribunal will not usually accept it."

Blatant, obvious and plain bloody stupid. They were

relying on my naivety to wind down the clock against my case by blagging for the time to sort it out, but why? Were they that scared of the case I put forward? It's the only logical explanation I could think of for closing the door on it and pretending it wasn't happening. Surely if any organisation had a weighted accusation of bullying taking place within its structure, it would react with a sense of urgency to diffuse and manage the situation as soon as possible, even if it was to demonstrate the accusation itself was inaccurate. My company just sat on it. The options at this point were to finally call my union, bring them up to speed on what was happening and how the company was currently dealing with it or continue to approach Jimmy and get him to do the right thing. As much as I wanted someone to take it off my hands I still didn't want to go to the union. Jimmy was practically programmed for avoiding it, and therefore it did seem a pointless task, but I decided I would give him one more chance to do his job right, and if he fobbed me off again, I would call the union and if I had to call them, I could demonstrate that every opportunity was given to them to sort it out before I made that call.

The following Monday morning I waited until about ten o'clock. Then I told Mathew I was going to see Jimmy as a matter of urgency. Sounds like a rude approach, I know, but every time I asked him for something like that it gave him the opportunity to say no by giving some bullshit reason like "we need these orders out and I need everybody on line", which was never true — he seemed to forget that I had a copy of the order sheet — or "sorry, but we've been told we've got to crack down on wandering about, I'll get him to come to you", which never happened. So telling him gave him no opening to cut me off.

Once again, I went to Jimmy at his workstation, and once again, he was looking slightly annoyed and uncomfortable by my presence.

Nice and confidently I opened with, "HI, Jimmy, how was your holiday?"

"Yeah, good thanks, nice to get away from this place for a while. I suppose you want to know how the investigation is going?"

"Yes please!"

"Well, as you know, I was on holiday last week, so the investigation was on hold. I've received an email from HR this morning asking how it was going, so I'm assuming you spoke to them while I was away."

"I did, as we agreed."

"Well, I'm going to be emailing the investigation request back to them this morning as I just don't have the time to do it, I'm afraid, hopefully they will pass it onto someone who has the time to handle it. Sorry about that, but that's just the way it's gone, I wish I could do more, but I'm absolutely snowed under at the moment."

"Thanks, Jimmy, I really appreciate your honesty because I was starting to become a little concerned."

"Concerned?"

"Well, yeah, a bit, you see I looked on line last week and did some research with regards to grievance procedures and what other options were available to me should I become unhappy with the way it's being handled internally. And one of my options, should all internal avenues be unsuccessful, is to pursue the matter through an employment tribunal. The problem I've got is the time frame for when I can submit a case is almost at the closing date. One of my options would be to open up the case alongside the internal investigation in case it overran, but that's not an ideal solution as I'd like this to be resolved in house rather than having to take it outside the company. Obviously now there is a time pressure for me to make a decision as to whether to submit a case or not and so far, internally it's got nowhere, do you see you see where I'm coming from, mate?"

His mouth replied, "Yes, of course," but his eyes were screaming, "You piece of shit!" at me. He couldn't even accuse me of threatening him. I came across as worried and totally ignorant of their scheming.

"Erm okay, well, like I said I will send this back straight away and hopefully they will get onto it as soon as possible,"

"That's great, thanks a lot, Jimmy, much appreciated as always, if you could let me know of any updates that would be awesome."

By two o'clock that afternoon (less than four hours later) Tanya was standing at the end of my production line holding a subtle smile on her face and a brown envelope in her hands.

She handed me the letter and said, "They've done the investigation, that was a quick turnaround."

"Funny that, who did the investigation in the end?"

"Jimmy."

"Ah wow, and he told me he was too busy to handle it, he must have cleared his work pile fast."

"Indeed, don't open it online and remember you're not to discuss this with anyone."

"Of course, thank you."

I went straight to the locker room, locked myself in the shower cubicle and opened it.

Dear Mr Allan

Following our investigation, we invite you to attend a meeting in the HR open office Wednesday (the same week) at 11:00 am to discuss your grievance in more detail and the outcome of our investigation. The meeting will be chaired by myself and will be accompanied by Tanya Harris (HR). Please notify us as soon as possible if you are unable to attend as failure to do so may result in no further action being taken on your grievance.

Yours sincerely

Jimmy McDonald

Weeks they'd held onto this grievance, then he'd given me a two-day turnaround once his plan had been foiled, not illegal, but it was so underhand it shouldn't be allowed as it was clear this was all a tactic and not serving the best interests of myself or the company. And what the hell kind of investigation could have been carried out, concluded, letters typed up, verified, printed and delivered to me in under four hours? A half-arsed, biased and vague one at best!

I knew I was being dealt a shitty hand before I'd even looked at the cards, and I had to tell Mathew that I had to be excused from my work and attend a meeting which was about him, but I couldn't tell him. He knew what it was all about by that point anyway, he would have been questioned as part of the investigation and he was friends with Jimmy. How embarrassing to have to ask him if I could leave the line to go and carry out a grievance against him, but that was all part of the ride.

# Chapter Ten

## The meeting

Wednesday morning had arrived, nerves? Plenty, sleep? Barely any, prepared? As much as possible under the circumstances. Every page of the grievance was burned into my brain by this time ready for their deconstruction of it, but I was finding it hard to function as a human being because of the overthinking and lack of sleep. I was too tired, but I did have just enough energy to be scared by it all. I was sitting in the waiting area outside the meeting room sipping the strongest coffee I could get my hands on. Mathew wouldn't have dared to stop me getting one on my way to a meeting about him, so I took full advantage of the situation. I left the line fifteen minutes early to get one and sit outside the meeting room. As I sat down, I could hear that Tanya and Jimmy were already in there talking. I peered through the crack left open in the door to see Jimmy had slithered himself into his best shirt and tie for the event; he never wore a tie, why that day? I put it down to a petty psychological ploy to add to the formality of the occasion, to make me feel that little bit more uncomfortable as I entered with my tatty and frayed uniform as though I'd been summoned as the naughty schoolboy to the headmaster's office. This aspect of his thinking was always so obvious, and it was laughable, it created the very opposite to his desired effect. In terms of appearance, I did the best I could with what I had; they were probably expecting me to turn up with my hair all over the place like I'd just rolled out of bed, unwashed, looking tired and worn down by it all, but I made every effort to look as sharp as I could. Fresh haircut, shave, uniform washed and ironed, best aftershave on but not too much, and I even went to the trouble of polishing up my old work boots. They spotted me waiting outside in the seating area and called me in a few minutes early, chin up, deep breath and I went in, armed with a warm, passive smile, a strong posture and a confident walk. It took about ten seconds of pretending to be in control to see Jimmy's confidence wither away behind his tie, watch him break eye contact as he always did and start shuffling his papers and hunch himself forward in his chair. I was bricking it underneath my put-on exterior, but he could be so smarmy and sure of himself; I had to try anything to break his rhythm.

The meeting began and right from the start he was so cringy that I surprised myself in being able to keep a straight face. The way he behaved you'd have thought he was some sort of actor playing a detective in a police interview room for a television drama the way he was asking the questions. Quoting times, dates from my grievance, reading them out like it was evidence he'd obtained in an investigation; it was awful. Tanya's subtle facial expressions confirmed it was an uncomfortable and embarrassing encounter. I really felt like asking if at some point he was going to charge me with anything!

He questioned everything in my grievance line by line. The shouting, the aggressive behaviour, the threatening gestures and body language, asking me to elaborate on each one. So I did. Then each time he asked why I didn't mention the elaboration before, trying to present it all to Tanya as though my grievance had inconsistencies in it, but after around the fifth time of doing it she had to step in and remind him he was the one asking for more information. I wasn't trying to add it in myself, idiot.

He then asked if I felt Mathew's rude and aggressive behaviour could have been the result of a lack of training as he was still under development and hadn't been informed on how to deal with those situations appropriately.

"I don't think so," I replied very calmly, "He's been an employee of this company for over ten years, he's been in his current position for well over a year so he's had ample time to refine his role to an acceptable standard where he doesn't become aggressive towards his staff."

Jimmy replied by saying that "we all continually develop in our roles and constantly try to improve with the ever-changing demand of the business".

I wasn't about to let this snake get his mate off the hook that easily by blanketing his behaviour in such a way. "Do you think it's necessary to go on a course that shows you how to speak to people reasonably and respectfully?"

"Well, no, not exactly."

"Have you been on such a course?"

"No."

"And how long have you been in your job, Jimmy? Three years roughly?"

"Yes."

"I haven't been on any course on how to speak to others without getting aggressive either, and I think during this meeting and throughout this whole episode I've managed to speak to others respectfully enough without the need for such a course."

"Indeed, you have," Tanya chiming in to support what I was saying.

It was a ridiculous argument, but I had to remain calm. He didn't want to get to the truth at all, he had already taken the position to defend his buddy and play down his actions. I gave nothing away in terms of emotion and instead allowed him to gradually unfold his agenda and allow Tanya to see what I was really working with.

"So what do you see as a reasonable way forward from this grievance?" he asked.

Reasonable? Throw the bloody book at him, make an example of him, to show others bullying and treating people the way he did will not be tolerated in the company and put him on the strongest of warnings at the very least. It's the wording reasonable I had a problem with, it's a term not even close to fairness. Anything he was going to receive as a result of the grievance wouldn't be fair, it would be reasonable, it was a mediation, not an opportunity for justice. The reality was Mathew wouldn't get anything close to what he deserved.

I had to make something stick from this, something that looked amicable on the surface but was enough to smear a bit of shit in his record and make him think twice about his actions in the future.

"I think speaking to him about his behaviour would certainly be a good start and a note on his file to say that you've had to speak to him about his behaviour and that this grievance was raised against him."

Tanya replied, "That seems very reasonable. The grievance will automatically be put to file anyway as a matter of procedure and an additional note to say that his behaviour needed to be addressed at this time. I don't think that's unreasonable at all."

Jimmy looked pissed, he was struggling to hide his anger as his eyes squinted and his face turned pink, he was failing his mission set out from Rochelle, mud was going to stick no matter what. He was most likely briefed to discredit my grievance in some way by Rochelle so that it couldn't be taken seriously, hence the picking apart all the way through the interview and acting like an amateur detective, but it achieved nothing.

"Would you be willing to speak to Mathew in a neutral environment? With perhaps myself or Tanya present to see if we can fully resolve this and move forward?"

It was a last chance for Jimmy to prove I was the unwilling party in this if I disagreed to it but, if I did agree, I'd be sat in the room with an absolute liar, granting him every opportunity to deny it all and provoke an emotional response.

"Yes, of course, I'm willing to do whatever is necessary to get this resolved, but both parties have to come to the table and be honest and open about it all."

"Well, in order for us to find a resolution and move forward we need to talk about what has taken place so that all concerned can learn from this experience and put it behind us."

"I completely agree with you, Jimmy, but if Mathew comes to the meeting not prepared to admit everything that has happened or deny parts of my complaint that he thinks may be too damaging for his position, then we can't move forward as we won't be communicating honestly."

There was no response from him. He left an awkward silence as he began scribbling notes down.

After about a minute of silence he asked, "Is there

anything you'd like to ask us before we bring this meeting to a close?"

"Yes, there are a couple of things."

"Okay, shoot."

"From the time the investigation appeared to have begun to the time it had concluded by receiving a letter on line asking to attend this meeting seemed to be about half a working day. Can I ask what your investigation involved?"

"Erm! (Clears throat) err, yes well … the thing is the investigation was concluded a lot sooner than we thought it would, so we were able to bring this forward. As for what the investigation involved, I'm afraid that side of it will have to remain confidential as we are dealing with sensitive information regarding other employees that we can't divulge."

"Did you speak to any of the six witnesses I put forward? Or did Mathew admit to his actions?"

"Again, I can't say, sorry."

It was obvious he hadn't spoken to any of the witnesses about my grievance. I doubt he'd had time to speak to Mathew properly that day either. Jimmy and Mathew had clearly talked it all out before the investigation had begun, but I wanted to know if that cockroach had come clean about any of his actions to Jimmy; he probably did, but Jimmy wasn't going to admit that.

"Is there anything else?"

"Yes, one more thing, Jimmy, I'm hoping I can get clarification on."

"Okay, shoot."

"I stated in my grievance that the meeting Mathew had asked me to attend regarding toilet breaks had been raised by Rochelle, and it was she who had the problem with my toilet

231

breaks and had passed it over to Mathew to address it."

"Right."

"Now what I want to know is, was it true? Did she have the problem and pass it onto Mathew? Or did he use her name to add weight and intimidation to his argument? Because if it was indeed her request that I was spoken to what's to stop this happening again?"

That angry little stare was piercing through his half-smiling face as he failed yet again to stop me. This time I was throwing his beloved supreme leader under a bus.

"It's a good question," Tanya added calmly, looking over at Jimmy.

"I'm afraid I don't know at this point, it's something that hasn't been explored but I will look into it and get back to you with an answer."

"I'm concerned that if this wasn't investigated there could be every chance of this happening again, that's why I specifically put it in my grievance. He shouldn't be using my line manager's name to threaten me with as some sort of intimidation tactic and if it was genuine, why couldn't she address any problem she had herself? She's my line manager, Jimmy, and although I've only spoken to her personally on roughly four occasions in the last three years, if she had an issue, it's her responsibility to come and speak to me, surely? Information could be lost by passing it on, could have been misinterpreted when Mathew was asked to 'deal' with it, I just don't want this happening again."

"Well, as I say, it's something I didn't pick up in my investigation, but I will look into it as soon as possible and get you an answer."

"Thanks, mate, that would be great, I'm supposed to go to

Rochelle for support in doing my job, I don't think it's fair that I should be threatened by being sent to her office."

That's right, Jimmy, go back to her with your tail between your legs and start boot licking!

I shook both their hands, thanked them for their time and left the room. As soon as the door closed behind me, I could no longer contain it; the biggest smile grew on my face. The truth was out there, my colleagues and I could look forward to clawing back a little dignity and a slither of respect while Mathew, Rochelle and the rest of her sycophants would be brought down a peg or two by realising they were not bulletproof.

Exactly two weeks later, I received another letter on the line by Jimmy marked "private and confidential".

Dear Craig

Following a meeting with you held to discuss your grievance (date) at which you chose to be unaccompanied I am writing to confirm the conclusion I have reached on the grievance you raised in your letter received (date).

During the meeting held on (date) you confirmed that your grievance referred to your supervisor Mathew Smith and how you felt you were being treated less favourably than your colleagues in relation to training, inappropriate language displayed to a workplace colleague and shown no respect by him.

I have now fully investigated your concerns, taking on board your resolution, which you provided at the grievance meeting. I am able to confirm Mathew has been made aware that all employees are encouraged to act respectfully towards each other as outlined in the company's behaviour goals.

It was recognised by you that there has been some positive changes in Mathew's management style and taking this into consideration would suggest that we all work together to ensure that any problems or concerns are addressed as soon as possible so that a positive outcome may be achieved. I would like to suggest a meeting is held as soon as possible with all those concerned to discuss this further.

I can confirm that I consider the areas raised in your letter have been resolved and this concludes stage one of the company's grievance procedures.

If you are dissatisfied with the outcome of stage one, you have the right to raise your grievance at stage two by notifying the HR manager within five working days of the date of this grievance letter. You should set out the grounds of your complaint and the reasons you are dissatisfied with the stage one procedures and outcome. An appropriate member of the management team as well as the HR manager will hear your grievance at stage two.

If you have any queries in respect of this letter, please do not hesitate to contact me.

I would remind you to continue to keep the contents of this letter and in particular the outcome of your grievance confidential.

Yours sincerely

Jimmy McDonald

As my eyes reached the bottom of the page, I could feel them beginning to fill with tears. Not wanting to let them or any of my colleagues see me cry I went to the bathroom to splash my face. Those tears were forming from no other reason than anger and frustration. Jimmy had skirted over every issue and had done it so blatantly it got my heart racing so hard I thought it was going to explode in my chest.

I wanted to walk right up to him and smash his face until it couldn't be recognised any longer as a face, pound it into the concrete floor in front of everybody till every drop of blood had drained from his skull and was soaked up by his perfect white uniformed work shirt.

He was essentially condoning everything that Mathew did by failing to address any of it and simply brushing over all of it lightly.

I knew deep down he was never going to sell out Mathew in pursuit of the truth or fairness; Mathew had too much on him. Videos of them snorting coke and Mcat together in their uniform at a party, even after they got promoted. I know because I saw a copy of it myself. They were even doing it at work, and no one ever said a word, I had to face reality; all my efforts and worrying had achieved next to nothing.

I never said his management style had improved in the meeting. Where the hell, did he get that from? I asked not to work with him any longer and that was ignored. I agreed I would talk to Mathew, so why was that put in the letter? To appear as though it wasn't discussed before and that he was the one that had put it forward? What about Rochelle? What about the note for file?

This letter had little relevance to the issues I'd raised, and it was done on purpose. He ignored my issues, so I'd have to raise them again in another grievance in stage two in a five-day turnaround, new notes and files typed up as well as stating what wasn't covered in the original. They were obviously well within their rights to put in a five-day turnaround for the second stage, but that didn't make it fair or right, so much more work, preparation and stress involved to build another watertight case in such a short space of time as well as stating what hadn't been resolved in the first stage. It was ridiculous and another clear sign they weren't interested in resolution, they were only interested in putting me off pursuing a fair result and protecting him. All that work, worrying, lack of sleep, stress had been for nothing.

I was back to feeling vulnerable instead of victorious in under five minutes, scared, alone and isolated again. As long as they had dirt on each other, they were always going to be protecting each other. There was never going to be a happy or fair ending to this.

When the thoughts of pulverising Jimmy's smug twat face had simmered, I began to remind myself that they were not the problem, they were merely the result of it.

Jimmy, Rochelle, Steve, Mathew, Barry were not the ones to blame, they lacked the foresight and the morals to be decent and appropriate people in their jobs, they were only as good or bad as the people around them and the system allowed them to be.

The grievance procedure clearly demonstrated it could be interpreted and manipulated to serve the viewpoint of those exposed for their wrongdoing, by being able to dress it as something completely different at their will. Playing down nasty, aggressive and threatening behaviour to a lack of training, experience and understanding, hostile confrontations to trivial matters, micro-management and enforcing someone else's unreasonable orders could simply be masked as areas for improvement.

The biggest problem in all of this lay with my colleagues, as hard as it is to say it. Nearly all of them were warm, nice, friendly and very likeable people, but sadly all had a helping hand in building the intimidating and corrupt regime that controlled all of us because they simply sat back and did nothing from the moment Rochelle came in. For all of them it was someone else's problem to deal with. When someone was shouted at or ridiculed publicly, they just took it, said nothing; those who witnessed it said nothing and turned away, they all cowered down every time, and over time the confidence of the oppressor naturally grew because it remained unchallenged, leaving the fear to address the problems to become greater and greater. Why not challenge them? Because their individual needs came first at the end of the day, and that's certainly not a dig at all. We're all capable of not seeing beyond our own problems a lot of the time, but sadly it is our downfall. Their kids, wife/husband/partner, mortgage/rent, food, bills, holidays outweighed the collective struggle for peace and fairness in the workplace and missing one pay cheque could make their life come tumbling down. If a person stood up for themselves or others, there was always a fear they'd be the next ones to be squeezed out of their job. To keep their head down decreased the risk of impact to their personal living, at the expense of the right thing to do.

The management knew this and played on it, being able to cut back break times, overtime rates and all the perks and privileges, knowing they would never be called up on it by their employees. We were all too fragmented, we didn't trust each other and began to only look for our own advantages that were constantly dwindling. My grievance could have and should have been one of the final nails in Mathew's coffin of his time in charge there if every person he'd bullied, abused, threatened and groomed had stood up in some way before me, but they didn't, and instead my whole grievance was allowed to be watered down, barely making a dent on his position.

We don't even seem to think about it any more. It's just something we do as normal as breathing. We get a job and the only gains or advantages we're concerned with are our own. The only impact we want to be focused on is our own. We never stop to think about the negative impact our employment could have on an existing structure. We'd frown upon being irresponsible in any other area of our lives, but it's perfectly normal when it comes to work. It actually sickens me a little when I see all these men and women on social media with pictures of their kids showing what lovely human beings they are with stills of them all at the funfair or at a restaurant as a family, waiting for gratification from others on social media like they're expecting to receive some sort of imaginary parenting of the year award from their peers online, only for these same fucking people to go to work on the Monday and scream at people, bully them and make them feel worthless or stand by and watch it all unfold on someone else's son or daughter. Decency is fast becoming an illusion in this country. We replace it with a pictorial fantasy online, showing the world only what we want to be recognised for and hiding our failures or lack of action without an ounce of guilt or regret.

All my colleagues had to do was stick together from the start, show their managers that although they were in charge there were certain lines that shouldn't and wouldn't be crossed. They wouldn't have lost their tea and coffee privileges, their overtime rates wouldn't have been cut, their trips to the loo would never have been questioned or monitored, holiday bookings wouldn't have been forced into a ten-minute break while other departments could continue to do it in work time and oppression would never have been given the room to grow as the fear of unity would have neutralised any ambition to do so.

If you show a bully absolute strength, you rarely have to do it more than once.

In the end I had to accept my solo effort to push back at them was nothing but a small, almost insignificant victory. No questions would be raised from it, and it was going to have no impact on the management and the way they treated people. They had nothing to fear, after all. The records would show I was the only one that saw a real problem with them but that wasn't anywhere near the truth; we all did. The only victory came from getting Mathew's behaviour on record. The grievance would be attached to his file as long as he worked there detailing his disgusting attitude even if they had watered it down. This meant continuing to behave this way towards me after the grievance would demonstrate it wasn't just a training issue, it was him and they wouldn't be able to excuse him any more, and he didn't. In fact, a week later he was so nice to me you'd have thought we were old friends. Don't get me wrong, there was no doubt in my mind he was probably slagging me off behind my back like there was no tomorrow but to my face, in front of others, he had to stay respectful to me, but it didn't stop him completely. He continued to throw his weight around with other members of staff, particularly a nineteen-year-old girl he constantly reduced to tears over the same things he tried to get me with. I know this because she broke down next to me on a lunch break. I told her what she could do to resolve it, by going to HR and reporting his behaviour, I explained how professional and supportive some members of the team were and would help her, but she didn't do anything. The second time she came to me and broke down I went to HR on her behalf and they pulled Mathew in for a "chat" but because she never raised a complaint herself that's all it ever amounted to. So on the third occasion when she approached me I was forced to ignore her emotions. She had to take it on herself. It was a terrible burden, and I would have supported her through it, but it had to be her taking responsibility for it or nothing would change for her or anyone.

I replied to Jimmy and HR stating I was satisfied with the outcome of the grievance but I wanted an amendment on the final letter to state that I didn't raise a grievance out of the way I felt as this would leave it open to emotional perspective and victimhood and it just wasn't accurate; his bad behaviour was a statement of fact observed by others as well as myself and I was appalled by it. They never got back to me with any amendment. They never set up a meeting with Mathew to resolve the issues either, they didn't keep their word on any of the things they had stated in the letter and the time had lapsed to escalate it to stage two, and the price I paid for this very small victory? Well, the management could no longer be so blatant in their attempts to rid themselves of me, so they went for my spirit instead, to break it, wear me down and force me to quit without any confrontation. They trained me on the hardest stage of the fastest line in the building which was the packing and testing section. I was left in an area totally on my own with no one to talk to, almost total isolation with only beeping machinery for company all day while everyone else received a fairer rotation system on their jobs. The packing and testing area left me exposed to the cruel conditions of the winter weather by the huge bay doors constantly open a few feet from my working area every day while my colleagues got to stay with each other in the warm. We were all supposed to share the testing and packing area equally as it was a lot more responsibility than normal stages. Any product mistakes fell on the tester's head even if another operator made the error further back on the line; three mistakes and you're pulled up for review; too many reviews your contract could be terminated. They made it very clear that I was either quitting or being sacked the second we made too many errors as a team. I tried to get out of the area, mentioning I wasn't being rotated as often as the others, but no one listened. Weeks and months of fighting to get out of there and be treated like the rest of the team went nowhere.

After weeks of facing off the cold conditions in nothing more than a t-shirt every day, eventually I gave in, and I left. I worked my notice, even though I had nowhere else to go. My mental health had suffered as a result of the monotony and lack of support in an area I despised and which I did way more than my fair share. My constant requests to be moved from the area resulted in me either being laughed at or ignored by the management. Even when I mentioned the effect it was having on my mental health. My physical health also suffered, especially in the winter months, freezing outdoor weather for nine-hour days every day with nothing more than a t-shirt and cargo shorts to protect me from the cold conditions resulted in colds, chest infections, throat infections, flu, migraines (not allowed to wear our own hats or jumpers). When I began taking too much time off in illness because they forced me up there every day, I was called into attendance review meetings and put, on targets. If it had continued, and I had failed to hit my attendance targets, it would have escalated until eventual dismissal. This is how they got rid of me. No matter what I said about the freezing conditions and lack of protection in those meetings it was ignored every time in the hope that I found it all too much and gave in, and it worked. I had been worn down emotionally, physically, mentally and socially until there was nothing left. I had to leave at that point because I felt so broken, I had no more fight in me.

Tanya was forced from the company a few months later when she stood up to her boss for trying to brush over a physical attack on a member of staff from one of the welding supervisors. The supervisor in question got four weeks' paid suspension, the member of staff that was pushed over head first into a metal storage rack got nothing and their case was played down to protect him and Tanya was pushed from her role as a consequence of trying to do the right thing.

# Chapter Eleven
# What to do

So after years of cutting back, sacking, bullying, breaking spirits, destroying people, buying cheaper parts, cutting break times, cutting overtime rates and being a ruthless mercenary to the very people she was meant to protect and develop Rochelle had actually made very few gains in terms of production output. Just over four years of treating people like absolute crap she accomplished only a four per cent increase in production, not the ten she had promised from her "impact" in the role, the hell we all went through, the price we all paid beneath her and it was all for a lousy four per cent increase.

For that four percent, she had made the company constantly tread some very thin legal lines, and on numerous occasions brought them the wrong side of it with regard to dismissing employees. It was only luck and the fact that the jobs were so basic in pay and had become unbearable that no one could be bothered to take it up in a courtroom because it was easier to find a job with similar pay somewhere else and probably with more perks.

Countless people with valuable experience bespoke to the company had walked out because the working conditions had become unbearable and morale had become non-existent. Supervisors of old, factory workers, engineers, HR reps, quality controllers, stock controllers all left after years of service to the company, some of them after over thirty years of commitment! (Thirty years! This should have set off the alarm bells!), all risking job security in an uncertain climate because they'd become that unhappy working under her.

Rochelle always opted for the cheapest materials and parts to build the products which resulted in production and testing issues. Various new common faults emerged on the products in an effort to save a few pennies but it all ended up costing the company more to resolve the problems created by the change which then began to erode the company's long-standing reputation for producing strong, good quality products. Cheap screws and bolts that rounded off and couldn't be used, pre-made switches that snapped the first time you tested them, we were chucking money away and slowing down the lines in order to fix the new problems.

She rushed through the company's new product launch resulting in costing the company millions of pounds rather than listening to the advice from the engineers and when it failed and had to be removed from the market, she blamed the very engineers that advised a launch delay because they signed off on their designs through pressure from her. She personally selected the internal focus group for the product, and rather than select employees who would deliver an honest and frank opinion on the quality and look of the design she handpicked people who were eager to impress and agree with her narrow-minded view and therefore cause no delay in the launch of the product. The finished result was horrendous, ugly and unreliable. She convinced Tom, the Director, to push it out the door, saying it had passed all standards and testing when it failed half of them and he carried the can for it and resigned while she was left absolutely blameless for all of it. Worst of all was her utter disregard for the company she worked for because the product failure could have been extremely detrimental to the family's squeaky clean business image if word ever got out; their image ruined meant all of our jobs would be at risk. She was one wrong move away from completely collapsing that business and if that moment ever comes, she'll do exactly what so many middle management cowards have done before her and simply jump ship, and leave everybody else behind to clean up years of her mess and damage if there's still a workable business left to salvage at the end.

Who's to blame? Short answer is every single one of us from the cleaner right up to the director.

The company hired her and should have ensured the impact she was making wasn't going to harm their company's structure or reputation, Tom was responsible for overseeing her decisions and act as a safeguard against anything negative or destructive she put in the business but in the end became powerless to her blackmail the moment he dropped his trousers and slammed her on his overpriced desk. His penis had cost him his twelve-year director's role. The staff working under her, and I think it's the most important one because we allowed her to trample over all of us, disregard us in our safety, wellbeing and development and the inaction of the staff to demand more from our boss simply wasn't good enough.

There's a real growing issue with just looking out for our own interests in a company and turning our backs on each other for a quiet life and a few extra quid earned in overtime, and it isn't just our teas and breaks getting taken away. Looking to ourselves and never the greater good has the potential to destroy the very company that pays our wages, takes care of our rent and puts food in our children's mouths.

Rochelle went unchallenged for over four years and is still being allowed to rot the business from the inside out. So what happens if she succeeds in destroying the business? No money, no jobs and no security for anyone because we willingly let someone burn our place of income to try and further her own career.

I made the mistake of thinking when I was a younger man starting out that if I got a job, kept my head down, worked hard, I could advance a little in a company and slowly create a better life for myself. The older I get the more I realise that it's just not possible or realistic to be able to sustain a decent job and it's not enough to sustain the environments that we wish to enter every day.

We all have a responsibility, every single one of us in our place of work, to ensure its future and it isn't just working hard that achieves it, it's the contribution to hold a fair standard of treatment and respect to each other, and it's no longer good enough to say it's somebody else's problem, it's all our responsibility whether we like it or not, or good luck ever finding an environment you actually enjoy or are safe in.

Standing by and letting one or two individuals poison the company we're invested in puts everyone at risk.

We all need to be vigilant and proactive in making sure no legal boundaries or moral lines are ever crossed and if they are, they are met with full force of unity and law. Bullies are shut down and shown early on that their behaviour will not be tolerated, that ruthless people who lie and ride on the backs of others must be held accountable for their actions and reminded a business is there to be sustained for all concerned and not just to be used as a ticket to a better opportunity while leaving destruction behind them in order to achieve it. These issues must be as big a priority as turning up and doing the job itself or we're essentially waving goodbye to the futures of everybody around us and if you're doubting whether your place of work comes into what I'm saying, use your family as the measuring stick to gauge the environment of your workplace. Imagine members of your family had suddenly picked up a job in the same place as you, would you be happy to see your mother or father treated with the respect your colleagues are shown? Would you be happy if your mother was spoken down to in front of everyone and humiliated about her toilet breaks or getting herself a glass of water? Would you be okay with your young son or daughter coming to work in your factory and let them watch their mother or father be shouted at and belittled in front of them? Their parents, their heroes, their caregivers and providers shamed in front of them over a cup of coffee or coming back from a break ten seconds later. Cliché warning! We're all working with somebody's child or mother or father and they all deserve a little respect for turning up, providing for their families and contributing towards our society and the reality is one day your child could walk into a job with snakes in every corner and you had better hope someone is going to stand up for them tomorrow because of the example we've begun to set today.

There are many ways that we can combat the exploitations and loopholes of the working laws in our country put on us by the lazy and greedy few who are too selfish to preserve something greater than themselves, even from the bottom rung of the ladder. This next section will be about the things we can do to fight back against some of these rising issues and take some responsibility as a collective to keep a fair and decent work life in our country's companies for everybody.

Middle management like Rochelle have to become the endangered species or we will be the ones struggling to survive in a workplace.

# Chapter Twelve

## The over-helpful temp

First of all, I'd like to start by saying that I do not envy anyone who finds themselves in a situation where they are having to accept temporary work of any form when they are seeking full-time employment, especially if they have huge financial responsibilities such as a family to support or a home to keep going.

I've been in the same position a few times over the years, not the family responsibility, but trying to fulfil my financial obligations with an uncertain income and unspecified amount of work coming in making an already stressful part of life even more difficult. Of course, back when I was temping the work was a little more readily available, averaging four-day weeks most of the time and although the money wasn't always great it wasn't far off full-time hours. Ten years later, recessions, economic downturns and "Brexit uncertainty", the temp life has become a different animal where you're lucky in some parts of the country if you can pick up a couple of days a week while you're trying to find something permanent. I can't imagine what that must be like for so many families, living within the cracks of financial stability; it's a fucking crap situation! Never enough to keep afloat but earning just over the amount that excludes families from any kind of financial support from the government, and maybe a strong contributing factor as to why nearly one in three children in this "great" country of ours is now living in poverty in some areas. Not meaning to sound condescending at all with that, by the way, I just don't have children or a wife or a mortgage, I rent rooms and lodge and have stayed too irresponsible to have those worries.

What can you do when you have a family to support? As a man or a woman, you have to pick up work where you can, particularly in areas where permanent work is becoming more scarce.

I've no doubt "temping" agency work was rolled out with the best of intentions in the beginning (doing my best to remain positive when I write this!). To allow those out of regular work to pick up a few days here and there until a permanent opportunity came along. It also met the specific needs of some employers who had extra work available for short-term periods that couldn't justify taking on someone permanently as there was no long-term business need. I've no doubt this made the government look like the "mutt's nuts" too! As these "temps" were technically in employment, no matter how few days they got, they drove down their employment figures as a result. Creating a very different figure from the reality facing the working class every day.

Another move that was given the green light at some point, and I can only assume was backed by the government otherwise it would have been illegal, was zero-hour contracts. What the hell are these things? And what purpose do they serve that temping can't provide exactly? Other than removing more rights from the working class is the only thing that screams out at me.

A type of contract where the employer isn't obligated to provide any guaranteed minimum hours at all. The employee, apparently, doesn't have to accept any hours offered either, but I imagine the reality of it is very different when employers have the room to guilt trip the employee if they don't accept the last minute, unsociable shift and almost blackmail them into taking it because if they don't accept it, they will most likely not be offered anything in the future, their working hours held to ransom. A terrible solution that again drives down the employment figures, makes certain tie-twitchers look good and offers absolutely no stability for anyone unfortunate enough to have to take such a contract.

Maybe, just maybe, I could be persuaded to see a very small point to their existence but only for very small businesses who may require experienced employees to come in and pick up the work straight away, but can someone tell me why on earth huge multi-million-pound corporations are able to use these contracts when their work is constant? And why are they allowed to offer out so many?

I know at least one major supermarket chain that dishes out these zero-hour contracts to dozens of people where the workload is clearly there to take people on in a permanent, full-time or part-time role but they don't, why? The best answer I can come up with is that they can use this method of employment to exploit their staff. Deny them the rights that permanent staff members are entitled to and watch the zero-hour contractors, squabble and compete with each other over any hours they can get their hands on. Like pigeons scrambling around on the ground, trying to hustle in on the little feed thrown their way. I can only imagine that it may force employees into a position where they accept shifts they might not want to do, or shouldn't do, on the basis that health or personal circumstances become strained out of a fear they'd be pushed back in the pecking order of being selected by the manager for future shifts. And when they are lucky enough to be at work, they will have to overperform, overwork, do more than what should be deemed "reasonable" in order to secure themselves another shift and stay ahead of their colleagues and all this for, more often than not, the minimum wage.

It's an absolutely despicable contract that forces people to work harder and harder for less and less while there is nothing of substance to protect them. I'm sure people will argue that zero contractors still have some basic rights but there is nothing of substance — it's left to the employer to play God with their lives.

I knew a lady in her late twenties, well, a friend of a friend really, and she had a zero-hour contract. It was for a supermarket in the town that was part of a major chain. Her job was to bring in, arrange and price all the flower displays that were situated at the front of the store. You know the low-priced displays I'm talking about, the ones that get absolutely demolished in a matter of hours every time there's a Mother's or Valentine's Day by blokes on a last-minute dash into the store trying to avoid a row or looking like a forgetful arse. This friend of a friend was quite good at her job too. She enjoyed it, going in and arranging the flowers, helping to create a good first, fresh impression as you walked in the store and she didn't earn a great deal for it. It was part time on the minimum wage, and she averaged about four hours on a Saturday and Sunday and she did it as a second job away from a care home to bump her wages up. She did the job quite successfully for about two years until she had a falling out with her new supervisor; then, all of a sudden, her hours dropped. She went from averaging eight hours a week to about one or two every couple of weeks. They never terminated or released her from her contract or cut her hours out completely. They seemed to use her just for sick or holiday cover until she eventually got fed up with her lack of hours and quit.

There was nothing done illegally by the company, but they could drop her hours dramatically just like that because someone there took a disliking to her when he joined the team.

## Temp to perm

It's normally a twelve-week minimum period but it can go on for much longer. I know people who have been held in this employment limbo for almost two years before they were taken on by a company. Why is that acceptable? And how do they get away with it?

You sign up at an agency and fill out on their forms that you wish to be placed on a temp to perm contract. Some will piss you about on temp work for a while to clear their workload, but hopefully, eventually they find you a placement. I think it's an opportunity for you as a worker to demonstrate you're a decent employee and a chance for your potential employer to see what you're capable of before signing you into the company in a permanent position, as well as the agency making a bit of money out of you at the same time. Sounds like a good system in theory that allows an easier transition for all parties but a system with flaws and left totally open to exploitation when handled by the wrong people. Dodgy agency staff who undercut the agreed rates with employers so that they can get to skim a little extra off the top and people like Rochelle who used the system to her advantage very well.

Rochelle would get someone beneath her like Jimmy to phone the agency and say, "We need two more." The workers would turn up and, if they couldn't pick up the job quickly enough with the minimal training provided, if they questioned anything or if their face didn't fit after just a couple of days, the leaders could and would get rid of them — no problems, no strings attached. All sounds brilliant from a company's perspective, I'm sure, a little more money to do it in agency fees but the minimum effort put into employee selection while being able to bypass employment rights. They could turn over as many staff as they liked until they found what they considered to be the right face. It's a system that if relied upon as the sole recruitment process, can have long-term detrimental effects for both companies and potential employees. As I've witnessed first-hand it has little to no immediate effects, it's something that's drip fed slowly into the business over time, unless of course you're willing to count letting go of perfectly good employees because you judged them in such a small window with minimal training!

When I first started at the mobility aid company, I came in on a "temp to perm" contract and my job was to assemble a certain electrical and mechanical part of a particular product. (I can't name what it is specifically, unfortunately, without giving the company away.) The process was full of circuits, wires, looms, cogs and tests and it all made quite an extensive build, so much so that the company had a target of producing only forty of these items in a normal working day. So, as a temporary member of staff I made sure I only produced forty-one a day. I could have built more and with relative ease because I was good with my hands and I picked things up quite quickly. I was experienced with hand tools too, which shaved some of the training time off. But the target calculated by the engineers taking into account all the delaying variables (parts coming in, retrieving items from other parts of the warehouse, toilet and water breaks etc.) put it at forty, so that's all I did. By deliberately going just one over their target each day I demonstrated that I could be consistent and employable, and it worked. After a few months they signed me onto a one-year contract, and I didn't have to lose any dignity by kissing arse to get it either.

To be honest, I could have built well over fifty of these products a day if I really tried, but I decided to space out the builds and take my time because I didn't want to be the new guy turning up and pissing off my colleagues by showing how great I could be at the price of making them look slack, but more importantly I'd got the measure of the leaders early on and I wasn't going to do them any favours. They'd have given zero thanks for my extra efforts but taken all the credit for the increase in output, making them look slightly and undeservedly competent in their roles.

After a few months of working well I was moved to another area to be cross-trained, to cover holidays, sickness and so on and they brought in another "temp to perm" guy to go on the forty a day line. A nice bright, young, positive and energetic lad in his early twenties who was clearly after a permanent contract as he was desperate to impress them, and he succeeded. A few weeks after completing his training he began knocking out between fifty and sixty of these units a day. Naturally, Barry was over the moon at the figures (not giving any thanks or praise to the temp, of course) because it was making him look like the "bee's knees" to Rochelle as well as providing him with a stick to beat the rest of us with: "He can produce these sorts of numbers every day, so why can't you?" A typical narrow-minded attempt at motivating us. Realising what a gem this new guy was and how he could benefit from riding on this young lad's back Barry immediately signed him up to a one-year contract and moved the line targets up to a minimum of sixty a day.

A one-year contract, whoop whoop! The ultimate achievement, one of life's goals ha! The next stage of employment in that wonderful shithole. When they offer them to staff, they really think they've given them something very special and actually stay there standing in front of the newly appointed staff expecting some sort of gratitude for the amazing, life-altering opportunity! In reality it's a twelve-month hoop-jumping period in which they keep a much closer eye on you. A minute late once or twice, if you called in sick one or two days in a year, if you stood up for yourself, or turned down the overtime they wanted from you, then your contract would not be renewed. But, if you were a good boy or girl and constantly did what they asked, however unreasonable, if you laughed at their stupid jokes and kissed their arses repeatedly for a year maybe, just maybe they'd give you a permanent contract after that. That young lad got what he was looking for, a chance of secured employment but he had now set himself an impossible standard by trying to build over sixty products every day. Where he was working so much quicker and harder, he began making more and more mistakes and the products were not passing the tests, the quality was suffering. The pace he'd set himself (and been encouraged to do so) wasn't sustainable. This young lad would turn up and sweat and sweat every day from the moment he began, working at what seemed like a hundred miles an hour and eventually, after a few months of this ridiculous rate, he'd burned himself out. The novelty of the new job had worn off, he had been broken by the demanding speed and was failing to reach the targets. His energy levels started dropping and then he became unwell and then he began taking sick days from work, a few days here, a couple there and when the time came to renew his contract they didn't. The poor bloke had burned himself out of a job and when the company ordered in another agency staff member to replace him on that line the target was at the adjusted sixty a day; there was no way the newbies could cope with that and there was certainly no chance Barry was going to drop the target down to a more reasonable level. Rochelle had given Barry too much praise over it. Barry saw any setback or withdrawal as weakness to his reputation and his insistence in putting the targets up had caused Rochelle to stick her neck out and override the instructions of the engineers who normally set the targets for the lines causing rows and department fallouts. Barry was too spineless to admit he had made a mistake, so he decided it was easier to get rid of the new trainees if they weren't up to the impossible job. The company started turning over "temp to perm" staff, two, sometimes three a month with some of them leaving on their own rather than waiting to be dropped because the speed was just ridiculous. A lot of these workers were decent too, very employable people who worked well and I have no doubt could have contributed greatly to the company if they didn't suffer the misfortune of being placed onto a stupidly fast line with very little training input.

A good quality product had become a cheap, rushed and unreliable piece of crap and the work could only be carried out by people who were willing to make themselves ill in the long term as a result of trying to maintain the pace.

The "temp to perm" work systems seem to be an easy way of employing fast and willing people who want to come in, impress and make an impact to the business as a way of securing a job for themselves. The obvious downside to this system, particularly when you have jellyfish in charge of the hiring, is that they could easily be drawn in by the "yes" people who will say just about anything to survive in that employment.

Between these desperate, wannabe employees and the narrow-minded cowards in the middle, a company could easily lose sight of realistic expectations from its staff or potential staff because environments are being created where lies and deceptions distort the accuracy of outputs.

All the temps want to do is to impress their supervisor, all the supervisor wants to do is impress the department manager, all the department manager wants to do is impress the director and as a director you just want to know your business is continually moving in the right direction and is constantly improving, you don't care how as long as it's legal but it's here in the cracks of this pleasing chain where the lies and misinformation can fit. Short-term gains for long-term damage, turning over decent staff, increasing targets and letting hard-working operatives go because managers are never held accountable for any of it as long as the output continues to appear right.

So what can we do as temps, workers and potential employees to make sure we maintain a decent employment without putting ourselves into these impossible situations and harsh conditions?

It's quite easy and might even come across as patronising but it's simply a case of not mugging yourself off. Having the discipline and foresight to never allow yourself to be the "over-helpful temp".

It's easier said than done, though, I'm afraid to say. With work becoming ever more scarce in certain areas of the country you want to grasp any opportunity you can in order to feel financially sound once more by going way over what the company would normally expect from you in terms of work rate and hours given, but what's the price you pay for it? Dignity? Pride? Self-respect? Your health? And more often than not, these jobs you break your back for never amount to anything anyway. You're not building your security; they're just taking your blood, sweat and tears.

The job market, even in the unskilled sector, is becoming more and more competitive, but we should not make it impossible for ourselves to survive in it by overworking and setting the bar too high on expectations. There are always going to be people in the world that will take full advantage. Managers and some employers are no exceptions to this, so we have a responsibility on our side of things to make sure a fair agreement is reached between us and the employer. You don't want to leave it up to the politicians to take care of this. History shows, that with regard to employment, the figures come first; it's up to us to set the bar.

Turn up at a good time, look presentable and professional, be polite and courteous but keep your dignity by working well to a decent and sustainable standard, don't work flat out to the point you damage yourself for a crummy wage, hoping it will lead to better things and that's about it, oh and always be honest too. Not just to keep your integrity intact but to keep transparency with your employers. They may not like you at times for your honesty, but you're not there to be liked and more often than not you will be respected for it.

If you're doing all these things, then you are doing everything you should be, and if it's not good enough at your place of work, then maybe it wasn't to be or they are not a good company to work for.

It's easy to say when your belly is full and your bills are paid, but mine always haven't been. Your principles and your values should never find a price, and as soon as you trade them, you're willing to accept something beneath what you deserve.

# Chapter Thirteen
## The power of the consumer

A hidden power, something long forgotten in our ever-growing and constantly changing communities. Something lost within a generation despite the ability to connect with those around us more than ever before. It is a dormant, collective strength purposely ignored to continue our personal pursuits of satisfaction by obtaining the things and items we think we need in this lifetime. The boycott, the powers of the consumer seems to be becoming extinct in this day and age and I think it's because it's an inconvenience to stand morally in a world where all we seem to want is the latest shiny crap and we don't want to know where it's coming from, where we even lack the virtue of patience, we want it all and we wanted it yesterday. The confidence a lot of companies now have in their ability to exploit staff, small or family businesses is bigger than ever because they know a lot of people will always choose what's cheap, what's convenient, what's in fashion and what brings them short-term pleasure over their morals and principles. Most people won't even bother to scratch beneath the surface of their latest purchase to find out where it's come from and how it's made, so the money keeps rolling in. One particular story, sticks in my mind when it comes to this subject.

I was round my friend Gary's house a couple of years ago for our weekly Thursday coffee and catch up. Gary was and still is one of the most honest, decent and principled people I know. He would never dream of letting anyone down. His word is his bond. A man of great character, he always stands up for what he believes in every time and always helps others where he can. A very solid guy indeed, and even this top bloke, whom I always held in the highest regard, managed to surprise me on this subject.

We were talking about what fancy dress costumes we were getting for our mate's birthday party and the one he was getting was from a very, very well-known delivery company that had recently been uncovered by reporters for the disgusting way they treated their employees at certain depots in this country.

"I'm not using them anymore," I told him.

"Why not?"

"Because of the way they treat their staff."

"What are you on about?"

"Didn't you read about them in the news last week?"

"No."

"A reporter went undercover and went to work in one of their depots for several weeks with a hidden camera and found that they were treating their staff and agency staff appallingly."

"Appalling how? What were they doing?"

"Instead of hiring permanent driving staff that would have basic employment rights the depot (up north) actively hired courier firms or self-employed drivers to do their work which left them with no rights or protections."

"So what!"

"It meant they could be sacked on the spot for the most trivial things, like having what was perceived to be a bad attitude and it was the supervisor that decided whether or not you have a bad attitude or not. Which basically meant they could drop you purely because they didn't like you. The drivers were set ridiculous and impossible delivery targets like nearly two hundred drops a day over a large area which you either got fined or fired for if you failed a delivery or ran out of time, forcing those who were lucky enough to find a job to work a minimum of six days a week on minimum twelve-hour days and do an impossible amount of drops a day. The set wages, van hire, fines and all the hours worked meant that nearly all of them were working for under the minimum wage and if they failed to show up, they could even end up owing the company money through van rental and delivery fines."

"Fuck me!"

"I know right, there were reports of some guys actually pissing into drinks bottles whilst they were out on the road to avoid stopping, falling behind and getting fined, pissing in traffic queues, then driving round with bottles of urine in their vehicle."

"Probably not their vehicle technically."

"You know what I'm saying, smart arse."

"Where did you hear all this?"

"It's been all over the news, been in the newspapers and on the internet, how have you not come across it?"

"Don't know, must have skipped over it."

"So that's why I'm not using them any more, I think it's disgusting how they treat their staff, they already make fucking hundreds of millions a year in clear profit, so there's no excuse for it. I won't be using them again."

"What, never ever?"

"Well, at least until I know they've improved the standards of their employment dramatically. I can't condone it by continuing to spend my money there."

"Yeah, but they do deliver in a day, though."

"Now I know you're joking."

A slight grin begins to appear on Gary's face no longer able to contain his sarcasm. Then he said, "Look, I get what you're saying, it is awful but it's not going to change, mate, that's just the way the world works. They make too much money to care about changing anything and they're certainly not going to rush around treating people better at the cost of hundreds of thousands of pounds just because a few people aren't going to use them any more, they probably won't even notice a few customers dropping off."

"What if everyone stopped using them? They'd change their attitude then."

"Yeah, but that's not going to happen, is it? People are just too selfish, mate. They want all their new stuff and they want it straight away and they don't really care how they get it or where it comes from, people just aren't interested."

"I think it's really sad, mate, because if the same people that are using these services were in the same situation as the people that worked for these companies, they would want things to change, they'd want people to stand up for the way they were being treated,"

"But they aren't, so they don't have to think about it, and, if it is as bad as you're saying, why do the people there put up with it? I wouldn't, I'd just go and find another job!"

"You're making the assumption there is another job to go and find."

"What are you on about? There's always work out there, you've just got to be willing to look."

"Doesn't work like that, mate, these mega sheds or super

warehouses, whatever you want to call them that are springing up all over the country are becoming like community work hubs. They set themselves up in small towns where unemployment can be really high and dominate the job opportunities in those areas either solely or between a couple of other companies that have also set up these super sheds. So, if you don't take the job, you'll be hard pressed to find something else and the worst thing is that these companies know it too, meaning they can take the piss out of people because they'll be unlikely to go anywhere else."

"It's not the only job, though, is it? I'm not saying it would be easy to find something else, but if it was that bad, you'd keep looking until something better came up."

"I get what you're saying, mate, but that doesn't solve the problem. It just means we'd be turning our backs on the problem, besides, if everybody did that or had that attitude, there would be suddenly thousands of people flooding the local job market all at once and those shit holes would stay open welcoming more unsuspecting victims in while the people that have left are fighting for the few available jobs and there's no guarantee they'd be any better."

"I would just go on benefits, then fuck it!"

"Can't do that anymore either, mate."

"And why not?"

"Because these companies advertise and affiliate themselves with some local employment centres, ticking every box with them to say they're legally abiding employers and never letting on what shit houses they actually are! So the employment centre is telling people there are jobs out there available, and those on benefits have to take these jobs if they're fit and able to work or they'll stop their benefits and the new benefits reform doesn't sound like it's up to much anyway."

"It is a joke. Why don't the government do something about it?"

"Well, from what I've read the company first of all flat out denied that all this was happening, then they were shown the reports and the evidence gathered from the undercover reporters. They then said the same thing companies always do when you think they've been backed into a corner of fault. They're going to carry out an internal and extensive investigation, which basically means they're still denying it and want to wait for emotions and the media to settle but if they know they can't wriggle out of it, they're going to pretend to be just as shocked at the top as the rest of us, pin it on one or two individuals in the management chain who they say don't represent the company or its values and get rid of them, in other words find a couple of scapegoats who were probably following orders. Then make one or two minor changes to their policies that takes the heat and media attention off of them and carry on as normal, not really facing any real consequence or justice for the way they've made hundreds of people suffer for a long time."

"Right, nothing from the government?"

"The member of parliament for that local area said he was shocked and outraged by the findings and wants to launch a formal enquiry but nothing will ever come of it as the company will get away with it all on the technicality that they were hiring self-employed people. What's left is a moral issue they will face which will be forgotten soon enough with a good marketing campaign and unless the laws change it's going to keep on happening."

"Well, I respect the fact you're going to boycott them, mate, but it won't make a difference, they're not the only ones doing it, they're probably not even the worst one to be fair, they just got caught out."

The reality is, as things stand, boycotting is the only effective way these major businesses and corporations who exploit the system will face the consequences for their decisions. Legislation can be loop-holed, rules can be sidestepped making the law almost seem inadequate for the business elite at the top of the pile who will remain reluctant to change anything unless it begins to affect their income or circumstances.

The only thing that seems to matter is money for most of them, not appeals to emotion, morals, setting a good example of doing the right thing, treating people well or delivering a good service or product really, it's just money. Getting it or not, and if they suddenly find they're not, you'll be amazed how quickly things can change.

Money is the power that keeps them at the top of their empires but how much power they have isn't within their control, it's within ours. Whenever we choose to buy their products or not, so why do we? Why do we continue to fund institutions that not only show no decency or respect to ordinary people (or animals in some cases) but actively abuse their positions to make the lives of others unbearable to get slightly richer? Gary was spot on with what he said, as much as it pains me to say it. A lot of people are not interested in these kinds of things unless it's affecting them directly. I believe we are all capable of not being able to look beyond our own immediate environments, which isn't a crime, it's human nature, the urge and will to survive. If we all lived every day of our lives worrying ourselves with every single problem or injustice in the world, most of us would have a meltdown within the first week. Unfortunately, there is too much suffering going on in the world for a single mind to cope with on their own.

I'm not suggesting for a moment that we man or woman or person the barricades (for the pc brigade among you) and go on a social justice crusade over every little working problem the world has to help towards justice, fair treatment, respect and better working conditions, because you're never going to win the battle, but there is something you can do... or not do. Don't buy it, don't buy the product, don't support the business that exploits others, it's as simple as that. What are you really missing out on? From phones to furniture, from clothes to cars there has always been in my time on this planet a constant need or desire to have the latest thing or gadget or stuff, even when it isn't being shoved down our throats commercially, and I've never really understood it. What I understand even less is that we don't seem to care what it costs to get the latest thing that's out, not just the money or debt but the exploitation of others, why? To what end? To stimulate ourselves temporarily when we enrich a very small group of people in the process and promote poor working conditions for so many.

It's never money you're actually spending each time, it's your small measure of power that you've earned and with it you get to deem what is acceptable in this world and what isn't. Don't get me wrong, I'm not suggesting for a moment we all start wearing non-profit making hessian clothing and walk around in recycled car tyres for shoes from this moment on, but we can begin to think about what it is we're actually buying into beyond the product itself and if we want to be a part of what they're selling.

Personally, I will never use that particular delivery company again or any other that thinks it's acceptable to treat other human beings that way. Even if the product I'm after is exclusively delivered by that company, I'd rather go without. I have to get up every morning and be able to look in the mirror and excuses just don't cut it for my reflection.

There is a particular brand of soft drinks I no longer buy because I was shown footage of dairy farms under their ownership where the animals are beaten, tortured, stamped on, trampled over, left to starve in horrendous living conditions and thrown head first onto transport lorries by disgusting creatures I don't want to even refer to as human beings. There is a UK-based sports clothes business that treats their staff like absolute crap, hiring temps, constantly threatening them with the sack over the most trivial things, supervisors shouting and screaming at them constantly to go faster until they sweat, bleed or injure themselves, mothers, fathers, sons and daughters all being worked until they are broken physically or mentally. Making them go through half hour clocking in and out search procedures unpaid, forcing these workers to go under the minimum wage for time spent in the workplace being checked and searched knowing there are no other jobs in the area they can go to alternatively, as all revealed in an undercover report put on UK mainstream media back in the summer of 2017.

I now think about the meat and the fish I buy, the clothes and shoes I buy and the choices I make. I try to shop as locally as possible, trying to avoid these huge supermarket chains that are renowned for driving down their costs with suppliers just so they can knock a few pence off their vegetables and force even more workers for their suppliers to earn next to nothing for the trouble. And I stay well away from any sports brands out there that think it's okay to own sweatshops in third world countries and still employ children to stitch their trainers and clothing. It's absolutely disgusting, and I don't know why as a country or a society we've allowed it to go on for so long, switch off from it and just pretend it isn't happening. And most importantly, I tell everybody about them not because I enjoy a good rant (which I do) because now I know I have the responsibility to begin addressing it with my friends and family whilst offering responsible (for now) alternatives; just don't be too preachy about it — people hate being preached to. You will either bore your friends to a point where you won't have any or get a punch in the face! I will never use social media as a platform to ram it down my friends' throats either and join the rest of the half-built arguments on there that bounce off against a wall; that only results in the op trying to appear like they're a decent person and relieve their conscience a little. I rely on conversation when the opportunity arises, built on facts and research, and I wouldn't dare raise a picket sign at a protest either; too many people have watered down the impact of a protest by prioritising so many different politically correct agendas. (You are ruining it for the real problems.)

I'm not perfect, very far from it, in fact, and there are many, many other things in my purchasing life that need changing for the better. There is so much corruption and exploitation flowing through thousands of products on our shelves, it's impossible to know every single one, but that shouldn't be the point at which we give up but the point at which we begin to understand what is happening and start making changes to combat this issue. I've no doubt it will remain a slow and ever-changing process. I will keep researching and make myself wiser as to who I give my little slice of power to and I'm not going to make excuses any more if there's no point, or it won't make a difference, or everybody else is doing it so why shouldn't I? It's not good enough any more. I'm changing my thinking and I invite you to do the same. After all, if some of you can avoid a brand of lager or a car insurance company because it sponsors your football team's rival, I think you can make an effort to avoid third world, sweatshop-made trainers produced by children who as well as being at huge risk are also paid fuck all in the process.

So after all that ranting, raving and preaching there's really only one thing left to ask. What are you going to do with the power you have?

Oh, and after the report of that delivery company came out they suddenly started treating and managing their staff a whole lot better and still made a truckload of money, so it can be done. It just changes a little faster when the whole world is watching.

# Chapter Fourteen
# Employers

It is you, more than all the other areas we've covered and are going to cover in this book that have the power and ability to stamp out these issues and rid your business of these corrupt and deceitful sub-cultures that lurk within your ranks and hide behind your company brand. You have the power to make a real difference to people's lives while at the same time ensuring your businesses are being held up by honesty, integrity and also employees who value your company and what it provides to their communities and society as a whole.

So what is it? What can you do to create a safe environment for your employees? What can you do to allow your businesses to grow things like trust, security and allow for development and innovation to take place once more within your organisation? What can you do that will allow honesty to flourish, maintaining a maximum and accurate insight into the state of your business as well as being able to sell genuine products from a reputable brand without having to cover up or paper over areas where you know those things are failing?

It's simple, hire the right people into your middle management. Stop hiring sycophants, liars, creeps and just slimy fucking dog turds who pretend to care so much about your sponge sales or the soft drinks you're selling! Start hiring people who are interested in developing other people and care about their welfare, start picking leaders.

It's so frustrating after years of being at the bottom of the pile seeing people who rise up through the ranks who have lied, cheated their way and stab others in the back to get the promotion and once they've got it are more concerned about who they think they are rather than what they can bring to the table and do for others from their new position of responsibility. And the frustrating thing about it isn't that they've beaten me or others to the post that were more deserving or worthy. It isn't a frustration at their status or how much money they're getting, it's that they've climbed up there to serve nothing but self-interest in a position where they have promised to serve others and the company. They don't know how to lead other people because they're not thinking of other people and they're not thinking about your business either, they're not thinking about the people who keep your business moving, they've lied to you, which isn't a surprise, everybody lies, but these lies are dangerous as they carry the weight of a business with them.

All these seminars, books, videos, lectures, courses and training on how to be a leader, how to spot them and how to pick them and we still seem to be electing selfish suck-up micro-managers despite the best efforts of leading gurus in the industry to point out why they are bad for people, the economy and your business.

So what is a manager/micro-manager?

It is somebody who focuses on the outputs (numbers) from the area they are in charge of rather than the inputs (employees). Managers will try to control everything rather than allow areas to develop naturally, control people, watch them closely, highlight every little mistake and try to maintain this control through consequence, shouting and intimidation rather than provide environments for their employees to grow and excel and work towards their full potential. They will lie and overplay their successes and be willing to take the credit for every positive action that belongs to someone else whilst hiding what they perceive to be failures or even pass them onto somebody else. They are the thieves of credit and the distributors of blame. They will make decisions, force cutbacks and money saves, never taking into account the impact it could have on things like morale and wellbeing and do it to appear efficient, business orientated and to try and impress their seniors at any cost, always concentrating on the stone that is dropped into the lake and never looking to examine the ripples left from it.

They will never defend those in their care against other managers or departments out of fear of their position looking weak or threatened. And also, in my personal experience, use their status to harass and sack anybody they don't like or threatens their vision.

Managers do everything for themselves and nothing for the good of others or the business.

So what is a leader?

A leader is someone who prioritises the input (people) rather than the output (numbers) because they know if they can create the right environment where people are motivated, trust each other, receive the right training and development as well as praise and rewards, the numbers generally will take care of themselves. They will give the credit of their departments' successes back to the team and shoulder any faults or blame on themselves because they know by taking on the responsibility of a leader that praise should go exactly where it is deserved and the criticism should fall onto the leader because it highlights areas where he/she needs to improve. Every decision made will be with the interests and welfare of the team in mind and they will always defend their interests from other managers or departments when criticism or change could affect their team's environment negatively. A leader will always create/allow an environment where mistakes can be made without fear of reprisal, knowing that everybody makes them at some point and it's better to be relaxed about them so that honesty remains, pressure stays low and everybody can improve and continue trusting each other. A leader will always take a personal interest in the development of each member of their team because they know their team will possess more knowledge, wisdom and experience than they do in certain areas and not be afraid to develop the team into more leaders. More leaders make the team stronger and more independent and a leader will encourage this rather than feel that their position is being threatened by the growth of others. A leader will always work hard, stay calm and always act professional as they know that to be a good leader, they have to set an example and not demand one. They will stay behind after hours to help the staff out, ask them how they are and care about the answer they give and always go the extra mile whenever it's required.

Sounds bloody brilliant, right? So why are you still recruiting the idiots who promise you better numbers, better results, more efficiency and laugh at all your stupid jokes? You're the ones who are number driven and why not, it's your business and you want it to be a success, but the numbers are your obsession, I'm afraid. People at the bottom just want to earn a living and in order for you to get those numbers and sustain them you need to employ people who are good with people, not the numbers. When you get leaders in charge you will get trust, transparency, motivation, a team environment where people will want to come to work and contribute more because they will feel a sense of belonging to the team they are in, which is your organisation. If you employ micro-managers who shout when the numbers have dropped slightly, who control every little thing their staff do, worry about the numbers instead of the people and take all the credit and never give out praise, only cutbacks, your business will look like it's improved for the first couple of years, then you will begin to lose out. Nobody will trust each other, no one will feel motivated to work beyond the minimum requirement, ideas and innovation will be suppressed, hidden and buried with no desire to share with people who treat them badly and if you push them for too long, they will go. They will take all of their valuable knowledge and experience with them as they try to find another environment where they can feel safe and part of a community again and the workers that do stay will have no interest in your business any longer and they will begin to drag their heels and the micro-manager who created this environment will jump ship and leave you with all this crap to sort out while he or she gets another manager's role in another company as it's now on their CV that they can manage.

Under Rochelle's regime she actively recruited the self-interested people off the line because they were the most disruptive. By making them the supervisors the disruption immediately went down, of course. The trouble is she now had no one to actually set a good example to the staff; they were now barking orders too and she went on making changes without thinking about staff morale all for the numbers game, and nearly every experienced member of staff young enough to start somewhere else left and the ones that stayed disengaged with them, dragged their heels and did the bare minimum for the business.

In my third year there, Rochelle had set each one of her lapdogs a new task or target for the year. One was to make sure that the health and safety incidents reports went up to demonstrate what a health and safety-conscious department we were, which I have covered briefly before. So naturally Barry, who was assigned with the task, began recording every near miss in the place. I swear to the heavens if you had farted too strongly, he'd have reported it as a hazard. Of course, this type of reporting had skewed the figures because he was actively searching for risks where there weren't any, but when there was a real incident like the time someone got paint in their eye or that young woman collapsed at work because of the heat inside the warehouse, it wasn't reported — they all turned a blind eye. The idea was to report the near misses to make them look as though they were preventing risk. The actual incidents were never recorded. Otherwise, the wrong figures would go up and they would look bad.

Anyway, moving on, Mathew was assigned with product waste and recycling for production, which went absolutely nowhere other than he put signs on all the recycling bins that were already in place, not a massive change to write home about, I'm sure you will agree, but he still made noise about it and Jimmy was assigned with space-saving ideas in the warehouse. I'm not entirely sure what his briefing by Rochelle was exactly. I can only assume that she said something like your task is to save space wherever you can in the business in order to make room for any further production lines and being the thick plank he was, took the saving space part of it quite literally.

One morning on the production line, roughly nine o'clock, I had only been in work about an hour, I look over my shoulder while I'm building and see a group of about nine supervisors and managers walking up to our little packing area, each one of them armed with a pen and a clipboard and also what I like to call the "serious manager creep face", because they only ever pull that serious face in front of one another when they're tackling something "serious" almost like they're trying to display visually how managerial they are, doing their best to out-manager each other by their expressions. It's like they stopped being real people and put on the act of leadership and I never saw it any other time than when they were in direct competition with each other. They stayed up in that tiny area for about an hour having a little meeting and then they left. The next morning the same thing happens, all nine of them go back up into the little packing area and when I say little, I mean it's about four foot by three foot of space which we used to make packing boxes and stack nine of them up ready in case there was a rush off the production line. What were they doing up there, I kept asking myself, and why does it take nine of them two hours split over two mornings? It's the space the size of an average downstairs toilet. What could possibly be so important? They came up and visited a third morning, not speaking to anyone on the team the whole time. We could only speculate as to what was causing such a concern that it required nine of the company's most fearless butt kissers to go up there together and put on a show. Well, later on that afternoon we found out. Just before our lunch break Mathew brings us all up into the packing area for a meeting. "Right, there's going to be a change in how you do things up here. From now on this area is only allowed to have six boxes pre-made for the packing."

"You're joking, right, why?" I asked.

"Health and safety issue, I'm afraid, it's causing us to lean out in the walkway while we make boxes causing a hazard to people with pallet trucks, we've already had several health and safety forms handed in about it."

"Mathew, what difference is the space of three small boxes standing up on top of each other going to make? My fat arse is still going to be in the gangway when I'm making them."

"Look, that's what I've been asked to brief out by Jimmy. If you have any problems, go and take it up with him and if you are seen making more than six boxes, there will be consequences."

I couldn't believe what I was hearing. Three meetings of nine people all with clipboards to save half a bloody foot of space that they couldn't use for anything else because it's right in the corner of the warehouse and posed exactly the same risks as before. It was so pathetic I was tempted to go up and laugh right in their stupid faces! I felt so angry at myself too, for allowing myself to engage in these petty issues at their low level but the argument was the packers actually benefited from those extra boxes. If there was ever a spurt on the production line, the extras helped the team cope with the packing and free up the line rather than allowing it to bottleneck at one end and fall behind; it actually did something. Jimmy just wanted to put on his forms that he managed to save some space, he couldn't give a shit what it did to the team or if the space he saved could actually be put to any use.

Later that afternoon it was time for the monthly briefing which was being held by Jimmy. As soon as the brief was over he asked if there were any questions or points we'd like to raise and straight away I asked what was going on in the packing area and why had it changed and I got the same crap as I did from Mathew. "It was highlighted several times as a health and safety issue, so we reduced the number of boxes to make the area safer to operate in."

"Don't you think it would have helped if you had spoken to the people on the line it was affecting as we could have helped perhaps find a solution that worked for everyone?"

"I don't need your permission or authorisation. It was done because it was a health and safety risk and it needed sorting."

"But nothing's been sorted, Jimmy, you've reduced half a foot of space so we're still out in the gangway making boxes because of the space that's needed to fold them and now we have less boxes to cope with the packing rush. I just don't see how any of this has helped or improved things up there."

"Look, it's changed, it's not going to change back and that's that! If you don't like it, you can always find another job."

"No, I'm all right here, thanks, Jimmy."

"I could make you make you build a box one at a time for every product and put the targets up and if you don't hit them, there would be consequences, so count yourself lucky we allow you to build any boxes up there in the first place."

The room fell completely silent as his composure slipped; everybody was stunned by his outburst. He hadn't listened to a word of what I'd said, he was more concerned about winning the argument than actually listening to the needs of his team and he didn't seem to care how awkward or stupid he came across or how much the change might have affected his team and its efficiency. It was all about being able to hit his target of saving space to impress Rochelle, that's all it was. To save half a foot and make things more complicated for the team beneath him told me he was out of ideas. A real leader would have consulted his team, talked it through with them and asked them to help him find any possible solutions to the problem and if there weren't any, which there weren't, to have the backbone to say to Rochelle sorry I wasn't able to save space in that area without compromising the flow of the line. I also found out at a later date who had filled in the risk forms — it was all the leaders; Jimmy got his mates to fill them out so that he could justify taking the space.

It's there in those hundreds or thousands of little moments, little changes where managers destroy your business. Most of them are not bad people. Jimmy is a ruthless piece of shit, don't get me wrong, but most are okay people; they just focus on the wrong thing, the numbers, they don't know how to open their eyes and see what's going on in front of them, they're too concerned with the numbers game you have given them. Leadership is a choice to invest in other people, it will never be about how they manage the numbers. Motivation, problem-solving and teamwork are things you cannot force, they're inspired by feelings, feelings that come out as a reflection of the environments you make. There's no process for it and no way it can be measured, but it's vital in a modern business that needs the ability to change with the demands of the market. It almost makes me laugh at all these leadership qualifications that come out. As soon as Jimmy, Barry and others obtained theirs, completed their coursework, they thought they were automatically qualified as leaders. They knew nothing about leadership. Leadership is the choices and sacrifices you make. Some of the worst leaders I've encountered often have the certificates and qualifications backing them to do so and some of the best leaders I know don't have a single certificate in leadership to their name.

I've mentioned before I played rugby, right? First of all, I'm not here to say what a superior sport it is and how anyone that chases the egg-shaped ball is holier than thou because they ain't. It's just something I love to do on a Saturday and make friends while I do it, but why? Because I enjoy the experience, not just the sport itself. If the environment was wrong, if I turned up on a Tuesday or Thursday for training or a game day on Saturday and I got told how awful I was, what cutbacks they were making to my membership, they tell me I'm not able to buy a pint or shower after a game and then tell me I had to play well or there would be consequences or they would start to question my membership, I can tell you now, I wouldn't have stuck at the sport I love for more than a month! So what is it? It's the environment all the players and volunteers create at the club. When I go to work, I just want to earn my money and leave and not dare stick my head above the line in case it gets chopped off. I don't trust anyone, I don't want to develop myself there, I avoid going the extra mile and I do the bare minimum and I also avoid my leaders as they have nothing positive to ever pass on. When I play rugby, I turn up to some pretty grotty places, take cold showers, leave with cuts and bruises all over and I am willing to break my body for the team, some players even fracturing their faces and we pay the club twenty pounds a month for the privilege to do so and we still turn up and want more the next week. It's not being biased towards it either, I love rugby because of the environment not just for the sport. I want to keep going back and breaking myself for the collective cause and paying them to do it because I feel part of that community. And my leader? A lorry driver with no leadership or coaching qualifications to his name, he leads by example and doesn't ask anything of his team that he isn't willing to do himself, a lorry driver who will ask how you are and care about the answer, share a beer and a few stories with you after the game, who finds the words and the encouragement to support you, not because he has to, because he has chosen to, he's chosen to be a leader and pass on what he can and inspire others and that's it, it's amateur rugby, he doesn't get a penny for doing it, the same as I imagine all other team sports to be and why we continue to go back to them.

It's very rare that you will find any job that will give you fulfilment in itself. Nine times out of ten it's the environment you create within the job that makes people want to be loyal, honest and hardworking and if you've got a job where the coffees are taken away, the breaks are cut, overtime rates are reduced, holidays are booked in a ten-minute break standing up at a constantly broken down computer, water breaks are monitored, toilet breaks are timed, people are micro-managed, pulled up and shouted at for their mistakes, if they receive no reward or encouragement, if the staff are pulled into the office for being twenty seconds late and if they see you drop staff like they're not even human, you are chipping away at the hundreds of little privileges that are making your company a good place to work and in the long run you will lose because the experienced and those with any self-worth will leave and it will be replaced by a bad reputation and a bad attitude towards your company and its products from staff who only want to take your money.

Pick leaders and send number chasers out the door for another mug to pick up.

# Chapter Fifteen
## Politicians

At what is probably one of the most politically divided times in our country's modern history, with the masses of taxpayers, low-level contributors and hard-working people being disheartened and frustrated by the inaction of our political classes and parties in the last four years, people are not only fed up, they are beginning to get pissed off. Lies have never been so obvious, certain self-serving politicians have never been so blatant in their interests and people are losing faith in the whole system.

Whatever party you're in or who voted for, whatever your stance on Brexit, I think it's fair and accurate to say nearly everybody is becoming more and more frustrated by it all. In this uncertain political and financial time people are becoming bored by all the promises that are not being delivered and now just want to start seeing results and significant changes that identify with the needs and wants of the people.

Do not despair, though, my paper-waving chums, there is something you can do to help restore some of the faith in this country... or at least promise to do so!

Ever since I can remember taking notice of politics back in my early teens (early 2000s) I started watching all the campaign videos, debates and election results on the TV and was fascinated by the whole process even if I didn't completely understand it all at the time, but one thing I noticed, particularly in the general elections, is there was always at least one party promising to increase the national minimum wage for the lower earners of the working class. Great, I thought, they're obviously trying to reach out to those on the lower end and pledge a better standard of living... but that was as far as it went.

Despite the fact that the minimum wage has never seemed to match the constant rise in living costs I don't ever recall a party or politician ever looking beyond the money question when it came to the quality of working life in our country. Why? Perhaps they can't really change any of the working laws and guidelines because they're controlled by the European Union. Perhaps it's a mammoth task that would require an unbelievable amount of work to change UK employment law. Maybe they don't want to take on the major corporations that really dictate our employment laws or maybe they just think that a little rise in the hourly rate covered most bases, but here's the dirty little secret, ladies and gentlemen, and pay attention to this: money isn't everything!

It's important, of course it is, otherwise why go to work and earn it? Getting more of it to cope with the demands of life is always nice and comforting even if it's for a little while before more inflation kicks in, so don't stop that, but it really isn't everything.

A little respect, dignity, security and job satisfaction could go a long way to improving the living standards near the bottom and changing and improving on our employment laws could go a long way to achieving that. It may take a bit of effort and hard work, it may cost a little money, you may have to give up a few expenses and pay for the occasional lunch out of your own pocket, I don't know, but you could make a real difference to those you represent other than just giving them what seems to be a bit more money when most times it isn't more money.

The very basic employment laws we have in place are becoming redundant in an ever-changing working and economic climate. Trends and demands alter in nearly every industry but the laws that protect the employees in those environments rarely/never do, exposing some industries to loopholes in the laws and guidelines putting ever more pressure on the workers as they try to earn an honest living.

Here are a few suggestions on how we can do more to protect our working classes, how we can protect a little more of their wellbeing. There're probably thousands more ideas out there that can be put forward by far more intelligent and educated people than myself, but here's a few to kick start it.


An employee is entitled access to at least one hot beverage per working day out of break times where the facilities and circumstances allow.

Obviously, this law change may not benefit all and I'm not even asking for the companies to pay for the beverages. Just provide hot water where the circumstances can allow it. Obviously if you're a linesman or woman up on the power lines you can't expect your employer to install hot water tanks on all company vehicles in case you want a cup of tea, but I think you should be legally allowed to open your flask once during that time (when it's safe to do so, obviously) if the temperature begins to drop.

Factories, workshops, offices all should provide boiling/hot water anyway and most provide vending machines, so there is no good reason why you can't allow your staff to break away at least once during working time to go and get a hot drink if they wish.

I remember once, I heard a bulletin on a radio station while at work, can't remember which station, can't even remember how many millions they mentioned, helpful I know, but they were claiming our economy lost an awful lot of them in tea/coffee and toilet breaks each year. Well, to that person and anyone who spouts that kind of bollocks or condones that kind of enslaving rhetoric I would personally like to deliver a big fuck you to your doorstep, you cretins, for even trying to justify that kind of drivel. It's a cup of tea, we're human beings, building things for other human beings in a modern, Western society! And we're in Britain and happen to like tea!

If you're telling me that getting a hot drink in work time (not excessively obviously) is detrimental to your business, then you probably shouldn't be in one, or if it results in you or your shareholders having to take a £299,900 profit instead of a cool, round £300,000 a year, then it's time to suck it up buttercup and make the capitalist system you're thriving on a little fairer before ridiculous moves like this on those who already have little cause the system to collapse on itself altogether or at the very least piss people off, as it demonstrates you have no interest in your workforce that provide you and your shareholders with that fat cheque at the end of the year.

You can probably tell this one really got to me when Rochelle got Barry to announce this change at work, not because I'm a caffeine fiend, but his brain covered by a smirky, little face didn't bother to take in the implications of that decision.

The poor man and woman I work with in their fifties stood

up by the open bay door in the wintertime, shivering whilst trying to work in the packing area. When it got too much one day, despite wearing the company uniform provided (not allowed to wear own clothing — it was a strike, remember) they asked if they could get themselves a cup of tea to warm themselves up as they were shaking, they were clearly chilled through to their bones. Barry laughed in response to their request, went and got Jimmy who brought with him a thermometer to check the temperature was above the minimum legal requirement and when he found it was, he smirked and said "no". Congratulations, Jimmy, all that power in your company-issued shirt and that's what you do with it. You let two middle-aged people potentially freeze to the point of illness and take time off which you held against them because you were technically within your rights to deny them a hot beverage. I went up there myself afterwards to check they were okay. I don't care what the thermometer said; it was bloody freezing and clearly not to a safe temperature. Jimmy came up and took the readings while the massive bay doors were closed (which only happened for an hour a day), he took an inaccurate reading and I'm convinced he did it deliberately to eliminate any health and safety warning signs and so he didn't have to take a backwards step on the hot drink policy.

In all fairness most employers in my experience and through asking around are more than fair on this subject, in fact, most can be rather generous with it because it's something they trust their employees to manage themselves, because they're adults. As long as it's not excessive or affecting their performance at work, then employers generally don't care; it's a nothing issue.

However, a law amendment like this could ensure the

minority of employers who choose to behave in such a petty way cannot do it completely. It will ensure those who can sometimes be exposed to the elements or cold temperatures, even if it's above the minimum legal requirement, can keep themselves warm enough to cope with it, have a guaranteed little moment of enjoyment, a little luxury in an otherwise crappy day and just make the working day a little more bearable.

A clearer definition on toilet breaks and the rights the employee has regarding taking them sounds like an utterly ridiculous notion, I know, but again, with the way some people are choosing to manage and supervise now it's something that needs a bit more clarification. As it stands, it's not against the law to question your toilet breaks because there is no law saying they shouldn't do so, they are able to question you technically, every time you need to use the facilities, interrogate you over your number of visits you have and how long you spend in there each time, which in my experience was always greatly exaggerated to lean towards their argument. The only area this could fall under is harassment, I suppose, but that is very hard to prove.

More and more employers are deeming all this acceptable behaviour to inflict on their staff. Of course, this is something that needs clarification rather than just an all-out law change; otherwise, it could have the potential to swing the other way and begin to affect the employer by those who would take the piss too often (pun intended).

For example, we could make it the law that an employer has the right to enquire on the general health of one of their employees or recommend a meeting with the company's occupational health dept. If they happen to notice that an employee is visiting the toilet on more than five occasions in a normal working day of eight/nine hours on a regular basis and it is affecting their performance. Only if they refuse the help of occupational health, refuse to cooperate, seek external medical advice or reduce their toilet breaks to a more reasonable level can a more official company stance take place and all concerns must be expressed in front of another witness and logged confidentially with occupational health to cover the backs of the employers and remove any chance of it being interpreted as a warning rather than a place of concern. Evidence must, of course, be provided that every attempt was made in the beginning of ensuring the health and wellbeing of the employee before any formal or informal disciplinary action was taken. Failure to provide evidence that an approach for concern was made or that it was affecting their performance could constitute any formal approach as harassment.

I can't believe I am having to suggest this, there will be people laughing or in disbelief that such a law needs to be passed, but I'm afraid that's what it's come to. Micromanaging fuck pigs spoiling the party for genuine, decent employers, I know so many workers who were questioned over their toilet breaks even though they did everything that was expected of them in a working day. It was ridiculous, but it goes on every day by supervisors trying to bully their workers, control them and remind them who's in charge.

I'll admit five times a day in an eight/nine-hour period does seem a little excessive, and if I was an employer or the one going to the toilet that often I would start to get a little concerned myself, but unfortunately everybody is different and almost unique in their toilet habits, so it's not something that can be strictly governed and five visits a day and say more than ten minutes each visit acts as a good buffer to protect both parties.

Having said all that it's not really something that should be governed in the first place. It should only ever be a concern at the point the employee's work is beginning to suffer but a definition is being forced on this issue by those who simply don't know how to manage/lead properly and use it to harass employees and make their lives uncomfortable as they can play judge and jury on what defines excessive times and trips to the toilet without consequence.

It's something that needs to be addressed as certain employers are looking to exploit these unprotected employee areas to new extremes. There was talk of Rochelle getting scanning cards for the line. You would have to scan yourself as off the line every time you visited the toilet or the water cooler, and they would record your times this way rather than admitting it was to monitor toilet breaks. It's an absolute joke.

I've even heard talk of a toilet seat that's been invented that's deliberately made to be uncomfortable to try and cut down on the time spent on it. What is the fucking world coming to? I really hope Rochelle doesn't come across this neat, little design as I can guarantee she will be buying it.


A compulsory fifteen-minute break as well as a compulsory forty-five-minute lunch break for anyone working over the thirty-seven hours a week mark.

The current law states workers have the right to one uninterrupted twenty-minute rest break during their working day if they work six hours a day. This could be a tea break or lunch. The break doesn't have to be paid; it all depends on their employment contract. Now again, most employers will go above and beyond the basics of this law anyway, as they care about the welfare of their employees and want them to get the appropriate rest to match the demand of their role and also in some cases allow employees to manage their own breaks wherever possible because it actually benefits their business. As before there are also employers who will provide the absolute minimum, right down to the last second, which is fine, they're not exploiting any law here, they're simply working down to the letter of it, but in some cases/industries the law has simply become inadequate, particularly when some companies now have things like a no sit-down policy in their workplace. Which again is fair enough, the law has to allow some wriggle room within it to fulfil the requirements of a business to be able to function but for those who do adopt a no sit-down policy, extended, uninterrupted breaks should be compulsory, if only for health reasons.

Research shows standing for prolonged periods of time can double the risk of heart disease as opposed to those who sit down and work. It can also cause feet and ankles to swell as well as compression of the spine and other things such as varicose veins. Now you may be thinking that the current laws in this country are sufficient enough to deal with these various health issues, but I can tell you from personal experience it doesn't. I'm not going to lie to you; I am a bit of a chubster and there's no doubt in my mind that the extra pounds I'm carrying around every day is a contributing factor in the health issues I'm now suffering with. The weight is my problem and no one else is responsible for that, only myself. I can't expect employers and the government to bend to my burger problems because I've let myself go, but I noticed a big difference to the severity of my problems after Rochelle had made changes.

When I first started in this mobility aid business it had a no sitting policy already in place. I got a fifteen-minute break in the mid-morning and a fifty-minute lunch break (five-minute hand-washing time) as well as a five-minute period before the end of the shift to retrieve personal items from our lockers, change out of our uniforms and clock out. This was enough. I always felt suitably rested from each break to continue working the rest of the day comfortably. But then Rochelle had come up with her brilliant and winning idea of stripping five minutes off the lunch break, taking it down to forty-five minutes, scrapping the fifteen-minute morning break and opting for a ten-minute break in the morning and a ten-minute break in the afternoon as well as removing the five-minute period to collect our belongings at the end of the day, doesn't sound too drastic, does it? Almost to the point you have to ask why she bothered to throw in an extra break all for the sake of being able to save five minutes each day. It wasn't enough time to build a single extra product on any of the lines even though that was what she was expecting. Barry had read out an announcement (as she was too spineless to tell us herself) telling us that research she had read suggested that shorter breaks led to assembly workers being more productive throughout the day. Being more alert and still primed to work, which would result in more productivity. In other words, not allowing us to switch off and relax. It didn't work, of course, probably because it was bullshit. If it did, it certainly wasn't to a noticeable degree, but the change from the "supreme leader" had been implemented, so improved results were expected from her rather than gathering data from the change. This meant Jimmy, Mathew, Barry and Steve put more pressure on the staff to work harder and faster to force a positive result regardless of whether it worked or not, but this was not the worst effect from the alterations.

The fifteen-minute break was the perfect amount of time to sit down, take the strain off of the body, relax and be able to switch off from working for a few moments. Take away the teas and coffees during work time and cut the break down to ten minutes, it's no longer a rest period at all, it's a nine-minute slot of mayhem. I say nine minutes because God help you if you left ten seconds early or came back ten seconds later; that was an instant dressing down by one of the supervisors, in front of everyone. You were not even allowed to stand at the end of your line and wait for the last few seconds for the minute hand to change to your break time. All these things constituted as strikes, and three strikes you were pulled into the office for a chat and threatened with a written warning for non-compliance. This meant the poor sods working at the back of the warehouse lost almost a minute and a half in walking to and from the break area. Once you arrived at the break area it was chaos. Forty odd people all rushing through into a small area no bigger than a changing room at the same time splashing hot drinks and food over each other, people nudging past or bumping into you, cutting you up determined to appreciate every spare second of their break.

Once you were at the breakout area you had to make a choice: did you go over to the locker room or queue in the line for the coffee machine? By the time you got a snack from the canteen lady or locker room and or got a hot drink and sat down five minutes had gone, four and a half minutes left to check messages on your phone, maybe take a selfie, take a photo of your snack (as there is also a no phone policy during work time) and attempt to small talk your colleagues and rest. If you smoked (which I don't condone or promote), you'd better have possessed lungs like a vacuum cleaner if you dared to have a cigarette and get a cup of tea and get back to your line before a strike. It was absolutely pathetic. Some people didn't even bother leaving the line and I think that was the point, to be honest. Whenever I came back from a morning break, I always felt clammy, more stressed than actually working, which is quite an achievement in that place and experiencing slight indigestion from where I tried to inhale a sandwich in about four minutes. I no longer had a morning rest. It had become a morning dash and a scramble. About two weeks after it had been implemented more and more people, including myself, started to suffer with lower backs and some of them were fit and active people. The company, of course, had stuck within the parameters of the law, but that didn't make it fair or right. When the issue was raised to the supervisors their only response was, they had provided rubber mats on each line to ease the strain on the joints and that was sufficient, but if you were more than ten stone in weight, it was about as much use as a chocolate fireguard, meaning basically our backs were now our problem even though these problems arose because of their decision and if we took too much time off with it, goodbye job.

A law change to two extended, uninterrupted breaks for companies with a standing policy would not even bother a lot of businesses, as I say, most want to look after their staff. Some would have to make minor changes but some need drastically shaking up when it comes to the welfare of their employees, and if their fall-back excuse is they work to the letters and minimum requirements of the law, then I say perhaps it's time to raise those letters and raise those requirements because some companies are just taking full advantage at the expense of their staff's health.

If it can be proven that companies require permanent, full-time positions in their staff, they should be exempt from hiring too many agency workers (cap per year) and should be encouraged to go through an employment/interview process that provides equal opportunities to both employers and employees. To stop this exploitation for turning over agency workers to avoid the protections afforded to permanent staff.

Six-month trial periods as clauses in any contract is sufficient time to find out if somebody is employable or not, so there's no excuse for temp to perm contracts to make up the majority of your full-time work force other than you want people to be totally dispensable and you want them to overwork themselves for opportunities. Temp to perm is a great idea in principle and should be kept for a few positions in a large company but when it becomes the core of your workforce, when your business or trade is constant and isn't going anywhere, there is no justifiable reason to be taking on temp to perms for two years before you offer them any kind of security. People need stability and employers should not have the right to continue to play God with temps so that they can be overworked before they're given a chance. Oh, and one more thing on this subject, and I don't care if it skews your employment figures, get rid of zero-hour contracts because they're an absolute disgrace.

Just a few small changes can dramatically change the lives of a lot of people in this country without making businesses want to pack up and run for the hills because of over-legislation. It's not exactly Champagne and swimming pools for the working classes, just asking you to adjust the rules slightly to make the game of life a little bit fairer. So the next time it's time to pick up a pen and start scribbling down the new manifesto don't just threaten to put the minimum hourly rate up if you're elected, listen to what people are saying, look to change the conditions and quality of life people are experiencing.

I think after the recent general election (2019), wherever you stood on the Brexit issue, it looks more of an inevitability than a possibility now, but I hope as a country we can look to move forward and face our future as a whole once more. And if it was the European Union holding us back in terms of employment law, we have an opportunity now to rewrite some of our laws that benefit the working classes once more, make history again by leading the way on how we treat our workforce.

# Chapter Sixteen
## Unions

Where to even begin with this subject. It can be a very delicate, complex, sensitive and even emotional subject for people. Where do you stand on trade unions? Do they play a part in your working life? Depending on your age, where you live, where you grew up, what you're taught from family and peers, your personal experience with them, how you vote can determine how you might feel about their existence in the workplace.

Some will argue that trade unions are detrimental to our economy when they become powerful enough. They can demand unachievable working standards and wages to companies, eventually causing them to collapse or at the very least aiding them in their demise because the company can no longer compete fairly or financially with their rivals in their respective markets.

Some may hold the opinion that unions are a non-entity, a placebo in the working environment that allows employees to feel a little bit safer for a little bit of their money but can never really deliver anything to its members of substance.

Some will argue that they are absolutely essential in protecting the rights and laws for the common working man or woman, should be taken seriously and invested in as much as possible as they strive to take a position of influence and act as a voice fighting for the masses that keep our economy and world moving.

I spent hours researching online, watching various videos, advertisements and lectures, then began talking to friends, family and colleagues trying to understand how the people around me thought about unions and after weeks of probing and asking around I found nearly every answer to be almost unique.

To write anything definitive on this subject would be unfair and inaccurate despite the agendas I may have and to push a particular viewpoint would be irresponsible because nobody can seem to show me definitively whether unions are a good thing or not.

The fairest I can do for this subject is to give you my personal experiences with them and allow you to make your own judgements and decide whether you believe they could be something needed in your workplace to restore a little more balance where companies and managers are beginning to go too far.

When I entered working life, I was sixteen and had heard practically nothing about working or trade unions. I thought it was an American concept that didn't exist here, only something I heard mentioned in American movies and programmes to be honest, makes me sound a little thick, I know, but no one had ever mentioned them to me growing up. It was only when I spoke to my grandfather shortly after beginning my first job that I learned a little bit more about them. He'd retired by that point but had been an electrical engineer for a city underground train company for almost thirty years and had been part of a heavily unionised organisation from the moment he started. He was very pro-union because in his own words:

"It stopped those pricks trying to take the piss outta ya!"

"Whenever a new foreman came onto the job the first thing they would try and do is make a good impression to the bosses, prove their worth, trying to push more and more jobs into us for less money."

"Try to get us working more hours and if the union hadn't been in there, they'd have got away with it too! I had my union card, though, one of the first bits of advice from the guys there was get a union card and it worked too because every time they tried it on, I could just say sorry, mate, union won't allow it, you'll have to speak to them and it wouldn't go no further. Because they knew if you pissed off the union, they could come in, close it all down or cause so many problems in the job it wasn't worth the hassle. That's one of the reasons I liked my job so much because right up to retirement I never got any hassle really, no problems, nothing. I was able to turn up, do my job and go home and not worry about anything."

He advised me after that conversation that signing up to a workers' union would be the best thing for me, get myself protected because some people would inevitably "try it on". As much as I love my grandfather and think he's a really clever bloke I was sixteen at the time and thought I had everything covered because I knew everything, I didn't need protecting, I could look after myself. They were different circumstances, he'd had a career, a mortgage, bills to pay and children to provide for whereas this was my first job, I wasn't planning on staying there and cooking fry ups for the rest of my life; it was a means to an end and I was far too busy thinking about how I was going to spend my first wages on loads of different crap (the excitement before the reality of bills hits you in the face!), so I paid it no attention.

For the next ten years I never really thought about it. Every job in that time never had an established union in the workplace and nobody was ever in a rush to tell me about one they were with, so it was a case of out of sight out of mind. I only saw my own interests and never looked beyond the world I created for myself and I assumed everyone was like me. If I didn't like someone or hated the job or more and more things were changing for the worse, I could leave whenever I wanted and find a new job and knowing this really made me feel in control of my employment. I never considered in my younger years that people could be tied to their incomes because of their responsibilities, therefore tied to their jobs. It didn't matter to me, but it mattered to the people that had to be left behind. Youth, time and energy were my assets and they were also the same things blocking me from the truth. If I knew then what I know now, if I had the knowledge back then that the choices I make go beyond the boundaries of my own existence, perhaps I could have made more of a difference to other people.

After the parcel company, bank and agency work I went to work with a family friend landscape gardening, so I was hardly going to start a one-member strong union against a decent, honest and kind devout Christian man even after all the falling out. It was his own little business; a union would have been pointless. When I left him, it was to go and garden for the "lady of the manor" and although I was employed by her large catering company on the books purely to be taxed officially, in reality, I worked alone, I'd spend days, sometimes weeks working on my own, I never really had a boss. She would outline tasks and jobs to be done when we spoke or she made the occasional list, but ultimately, I was responsible for myself, I managed my own break times and working hours. I just had to make sure the property was up together, so again the requirement for a union in those circumstances seemed redundant.

It was only after I arrived at the mobility aids company that I began to look into it, and even then, it wasn't straight away. I was there for just over two years before I had the desire to seek out union representation. Don't get me wrong, in that time I had seen many things change, more and more of the privileges were being stripped away from us, the warehouse staff and morale were plunging deeper and deeper into darkness and I was never happy about any of it, but I didn't act straight away. I suppose when I look back on it there was a hesitation, I was finding it hard to be the one to make the stand. I was the junior member of the team, I was hoping the more experienced members of the team, the lifers or the ones who had been there at least ten years or more (and there was plenty of them left) would stand up and be counted, say something, anything when all the changes became too much, but they never did, despite all their inward complaining and bitching to each other.

It was only when I was moved by Barry over to Mathew's line (after the coffee restrictions) that I realised unless I took some sort of action it could be the beginning of the end for me at that place. That's why I had been moved after all; that grotesque, snivelling sack of crap had the reputation of being able to squeeze people out of the business with his nastiness, bullying and mistreatment of others. He was the go-to guy for that. If any of the supervisors ever had a problem with one of their staff, they would transfer them over to Mathew's line so he could begin to destroy them in any way he could short of physical violence and he got a major kick out of holding that reputation too as he enjoyed breaking people's spirits, but mainly it was to continue pleasing Rochelle and staying in her good books. So I knew going over to his line for "retraining" was for one reason and one reason only, to get rid of me. I knew I had a big target on my back, I just couldn't prove it. Despite all the creeps that were put in charge of production I didn't want to leave, as strange as that sounds. The job itself was okay, it wasn't complicated and it was intricate enough to keep my mind occupied. My body was going to start betraying me anytime soon, starting to put limitations on what I'd physically be able to do after years of rugby and manual work and most of all, I liked a lot of the people that I worked with. The majority of them were nice, decent, honest, humble people who wanted to earn for the simple life, so why should I leave? There were just a few bad apples in the business, the owner was a good guy who put a strong emphasis on being like a family and it was the bad apples turning away from that message, not me. I was a bloody good worker, so I had absolutely no intention of leaving, but I was being backed into a corner and pushed into the spider's web, so I had to do something to fight back and quick.

I spoke to friends and family about what was happening and what my options were, leave being the obvious one put forward by most, but then my cousin suggested joining a union. I began enquiring at work, asking colleagues about unions. Some would laugh at me, some were completely clueless not unlike myself and some would say things like, "This company does not recognise a union, mate, don't waste your time," which I thought was a strange thing to say. I didn't think it was legal to simply ignore unions, otherwise how would they even get into a workplace? How could they exist? I can't imagine many companies actively opting for someone else to be at the negotiating table.

So I went to the supervisors and managers to see if they could provide any information and they said the same thing, "This company will not recognise a union, so don't waste your time and money."

I went to the HR department and asked them about it. After their complete look of confusion as if to say why do you need one when we're so corrupt but fantastic they actually responded with, "We don't have a union and the company doesn't want one either!"

Everybody who was in some sort of authority in the company was so defensive and wouldn't answer my questions about a union membership, I just kept getting the brush off or a door shut in my face, so I went home and began to research it online, I researched trade unions and how companies were simply able to opt out of it. After an hour or so (being distracted by funny animal videos!) I came across an article explaining how unions could be recognised by law in the workplace.

1. The union must ask the company to recognise them voluntarily. If the company agrees to the request then the union is recognised.

2. The union can apply for recognition by providing information to the CAC if, ten per cent of a bargaining unit have union membership or, they can provide evidence that the majority of employees are in favour of union recognition. (CAC - Central Arbitration Committee)."

The way it was being implied by the suck ups at the company, there was no point in me joining one as they didn't recognise one. Therefore, it would be a pointless task. They didn't tell me I could still join one legally regardless of whether the company recognised it officially or not (given the way they treated people they were hardly likely to), so I began researching what a union membership could offer me outside a recognised agreement with the company.

First of all, I could not be sacked or dismissed for joining an unrecognised union from my place of work or looking to join one, or even taking part in union activities. I could join a union on my own that represented the industry I was working in despite a lack of recognition from the company. The refusal of the company's acknowledgement meant that the union wouldn't be allowed into the company or at the negotiating table in terms of pay, working conditions and benefits, but there were still a few things they could offer from that position.

- Free legal advice covered and provided by the membership
- Representation in any formal grievance or disciplinary raised against the union member
- Legal cover in the thousands (variations between different organisations) in the event of a works tribunal being raised against the member or the company.

Given the circumstances beginning to grow around me it seemed like the obvious solution. As is said I couldn't prove anything at that point, of course, but that was fine because the union wouldn't advise, consult or represent me for anything predating my membership but it would be in place for any provable corruption or bullying after the date of my membership acceptance, and I knew it was going to happen, there was no question. There may not have been anything technically wrong or illegal in what Mathew and Barry were doing at that point, but the motives for transferring me were very clear.

I began looking through various different union websites trying to find the organisation that best suited my job description. Then I came across a search engine that specialises in finding the best union for me. I typed in all my details about my work and where I lived and within seconds it came up with a page of the unions best suited to my job. I contacted a few of them by phone and asked if they could send me their information packs. After reading through everything they had to offer, I found what looked to be the most ideal one. It covered assembly and factory workers/operators and was roughly twelve pound a month and the membership came with a big benefits bundle including:

- Discounted car insurance
- Discounted life cover
- Discounted white goods
- Free use of the union's convalescent home down near Devon for any member on long-term sick from their employment
- Funeral, credit and savings schemes
- Representation at hearings with option to move hearing dates should union representatives be unavailable
- Free twenty-four-hour legal helpline
- Education and training on promoting and protecting collective workplace interests.

I filled out and posted the application form of my chosen union and immediately felt a little bit safer. I even felt a little smug as well. There was a question on the form asking whether or not I'd like them to inform the company I had joined with them; that got a nice big tick in the box.

For the next four or five days at work, I continued to take crap off Mathew. He was breathing down my neck any moment he had free, watching me like a hawk, no one else, just me, waiting to pounce on any little mistake I could make despite the fact I was training in what was supposed to be a pressure free environment. He put me at a stage next to one of the young vulnerable girls he was grooming so he could come along and cheese on her while being able to keep an eye on me, call me out constantly and embarrass me in front of the new team. He made it blatantly obvious he was going to treat me differently to the rest of the staff under his control, but then suddenly it stopped. I began to not see him at all after the morning brief. He didn't come near me, he didn't speak to me and didn't even come near to my part of my line, not even to hit on the new, young temps. The eagle had landed. I could tell the moment they were notified of my new membership because every manager and supervisor began giving me funny looks, and it wasn't paranoia either. If I'd walk past them while they were in conversation, they'd suddenly stop and stare at me and colleagues were even picking up on it. I don't think for a moment that they were suddenly frightened of me. I think Rochelle had warned them off me because the union was an immeasurable power to them and her, and no one wanted to be the guy or girl that unleashed it on her, which all was confirmation that I had made the right decision, otherwise why hold a meeting over something so insignificant as somebody joining an unrecognised union? It shouldn't have even been a bead of sweat on their foreheads and if they were a decent company, it shouldn't have even come up in conversation as they would have nothing to worry about, but they did, so they knew what they were doing to their staff was wrong, if not legally then certainly morally and definitely putting the squeaky-clean reputation of the company at stake.

All the steps back from me and a fear to engage in his bullying only lasted for a couple of weeks, unfortunately. The pressure of Rochelle finally got to Mathew to micro-manage us and he picked up exactly where he had left off, back to the snide comments, swearing at myself and the rest of the team and shouting at me in front of other members of staff. The only difference was I was recording every confrontation, times, dates, witnesses, what had happened and what was said, knowing I could now share my concerns with an external body if I needed to. When his bullying failed to have the desired effect he eventually snapped completely, which is when he pulled me and another staff member into the office to shout at the top of his voice at us, snarling, swearing and getting really aggressive and starting to lose control over my toilet breaks, which is what led to the grievance I raised against him.

Once the grievance began, I would like to say the union were really effective and were able to help me, but sadly that wasn't the case. Their legal helpline was very friendly, and professional, but they couldn't help me because technically they weren't breaking any laws in questioning my toilet breaks. The aggressive behaviour shown by Mathew could have been up for grabs, I'm sure, I even had a witness, but I knew he would have lied and really dragged out the process. I knew the union could come in and represent me in some capacity over the issue and shame the whole thing for what it was... dog shit, but, there was no point, If there was no hard evidence he could just wriggle his way out of it, witnesses or not. Most of his employees would have been too afraid to come forward meaning it would have boiled down to my word against his.

So how do I summarise my experience with a union and their effectiveness? They were a great deterrent against bullies; every manager or supervisor thought twice before acting on their desires to push me out of the company as it stayed an unknown power there to protect me, but the reality of that power, I'm afraid to say, is rather different from any preconceptions they may have. There isn't a great deal the union can do in a non-unionised workplace. They can provide great legal advice, they can cover my legal costs at a tribunal, they can even offer me great discounts on my own funeral (depending who you sign up with), they can even represent me in a disciplinary, but they can't shield me from exposure to nasty, hateful self-interested puppies who enjoy putting you down and try their very best to remove you from an organisation where you've earned your right to be there.

The truth is they will only ever be as good as the laws they can uphold, and as it stands there's a lot of open ground they just cannot cover making for little impact on corrupt organisations.

Saying all of that, on the whole, I would still recommend joining a union in my personal opinion, I just don't want anyone to have a warped perception of what they can offer. I believe them to be a necessary evil in a country where corruption has so much room to grow and ill gains are becoming so common it's now normalised. They can educate you on your laws and rights, protect you financially if you have to enter a courtroom, offer you a great discount on a tumble dryer if you need one (depending on your membership), they could even assist with promotion opportunities if you are a suitable candidate, negotiate better rates of pay and safer work practices if the company had to officially recognise them. They will act as a last line of defence if you're ever disciplined rightly or wrongly to try and prevent any unfair dismissal and to make sure the law is being upheld to the letter when you're being managed or supervised.

But, what's more important than all of that is what you're paying forward... or trying to. You as an ordinary employee are taking responsibility for your workplace and the people you work with by trying to ensure there is something within that organisation that has their interests and protection as a priority. Your membership, no matter what lovely perks it may offer you personally, will always serve a greater interest than your own benefit. It's saying you want to make a difference to everybody, not just yourself, it's saying you want a fairer and more just environment where anybody you grow to care about can be taken advantage of and you're willing to invest in their wellbeing and improving and protecting it as well as your own.

Since I joined a union, I have made many attempts over the last couple of years to recruit others into a membership but to no avail. A few of my colleagues were intimidated by the threat the owners made to move the company out of the country and relocate in mainland Europe should a union ever rise within the business. Most were put off by the twelve pound a month membership, twelve pound a month! I'm not joking either. A lot of them spend that on two nights' worth of weed to inhale in a bid to block out what a shitty existence they have. How about you put it towards something more positive and productive, you fuck wits? Change your world and the world of others rather than fund the way you accept it! I wouldn't mind, it is a free choice after all, but all those that turned their noses up at paying the three pound per week are the ones that always moan first and loudest when the middle management come in and take away one of the few remaining privileges we have left, but when they are presented with a solution to negotiate better working conditions suddenly their arseholes tighten up.

For as long as I remained at the company I kept pushing and encouraging for membership there, right up until I left. Not because I wanted to make life difficult for the owners, but they had left us with no choice. I couldn't stand to see fifty-year-old men and women squeezed out of the company they'd spent years loyal to because they were starting to slow down a bit. These are the people we need to protect, that we need knowledge and advice for and because one day we will be in their shoes if we're lucky enough to get to that age and I hope somebody will help me fight my corner when I start to enter a scary and potentially vulnerable part of my life.

In my opinion a union, recognised or unrecognised, might not be able to offer you an easy or at times an effective solution but it's one of the only weapons we have to protect us and we should all do what we can to make it as effective as possible to benefit everybody and maintain an honest and fair environment.

# Chapter Seventeen
# Rounding up

What is work or a job supposed to be in the end? A place where we can contribute to our society and to receive the benefits of that job that reflect the contributions we are making. That's it! The rest of it is just political, overcomplicated, built up, status-chasing bullshit really.

Movies, stories, social media, books, programmes, reality TV shows can all create an image that the world is some sort of commercial, financial and successful ladder that's just waiting to be climbed, to a paradise reserved for everyone worthy, and we must climb it too! We have to climb it! There's no choice. It's the only thing we're born to do. It's the biggest lie ever that's ever been rammed down our throats every day. You know what? There's absolutely nothing wrong with just earning a good living while seeking to find a level of peace and contentment in our lives. That is not only our right but an ideal. Happiness and complete fulfilment are not something on the shelf waiting to be bought by anyone that can afford it once they get to a certain point of success in their journey. Life just doesn't work like that, happiness is not everyone's right and I really believe chasing money, fame and status isn't the way to get there either. Don't get me wrong, there is nothing wrong with self-improvement at all. Everybody should look to constantly improve and better themselves and reach their full potential and success should be a bi-product of that self-improvement. The finish line should never be the be all and end all of our lives, otherwise we'll miss out on what's going on in the middle.

There's this big thing in the media at the time of writing this and people seem to be lapping it up like thirsty dogs after a long walk about "millennials" and "gen z's" being lazy and entitled generations. Softer mentally than the generations that preceded them and forever whining about work and rights rather than rolling up their sleeves and getting on with it instead of chasing ideals. It's just not true. A lot has changed over the last thirty years, wages earned in this country don't get you nearly as far as they used to, everything from homes to shopping has blown up in price and workers' security and rights have been watered down through employment technicalities. Don't get me wrong, there are probably quite a few of the younger generations that do fit that description, but are you honestly telling me that you would tolerate all the things I've covered in this book and call it a decent place to work? You'd just roll up your sleeves and never complain about any of it? I call bullshit on that if you said yes.

So with more and more working environments like the ones I've covered, popping up everywhere in our country, how on earth do you expect anyone, not just "millennials" or "gen z's" to go to work and feel motivated? To be enthusiastic, inspired and take our country forward with innovation and development?

These are environments with no loyalty, reward, respect or trust, and we want to stick people in these environments that display some of the worst human traits we possess and say "get on with it", "count your blessings" and expect them to be happy with their lot.

Personally, I've never bought into the whole success, climb the ladder and shoot for the stars stuff, it just wasn't for me, particularly when I've seen years of how low people will stoop to for a shot at it. If that's your aim, that is your right and your privilege but so is mine not to, so where do I fit in? And the thousands of others who just want a normal, quiet life? I've tried to keep my head down, but I can't seem to be left alone. People want to use my back to climb up and latch onto the ladder to pull themselves up and they do it by making me work harder and faster constantly and adding more and more pressure to my workload while removing my perks and threatening me with my employment if I don't conform.

I just want to earn an honest wage and be left to do it in an environment where I'm not constantly threatened with my job's security. It doesn't have to be an exciting job, it doesn't have to be filled with loads of career opportunities and a massive wage packet, just somewhere I can earn a living, do my job well and go home without all the bullying and bullshit. Does such a place still exist? If it does, then give me a shout!

I've already said it before in the book, we can't keep blaming the guys at the top for the social and brutal shit bucket a lot of us seem to be sitting in. Politicians, CEOs, directors, business owners are indeed responsible for what goes on in their business too, but it's not their doing. They can't run the entire business from the top, particularly in worldwide companies; it's just not possible. Ultimately, they have to put their trust in the right people in middle management for the day-to-day running of the company and they don't always employ well every time, they're human too and they're lied to and made false promises by the idiots in the middle.

It's us at the bottom, we're responsible for this mess! If we're in that company and happy to take wages from it, then it's also our duty to ensure it's run the right way, too. Middle management will only ever be as good or as corrupt as we, the workforce, allow them to be, and more often than not, we seem happy enough to accept the latter. Why is that? Is it because we all love a bit of division and drama in the ranks? Or on some subconscious level do we enjoy being enslaved or downtrodden?

We constantly fail to see strength in numbers or identify any kind of unity with those around us struggling with the same issues. We all seem too afraid to stick our hands up at work or speak to our colleagues and ask, "Do you agree with this?", "Do you think this is right?", "How do you feel about this?" And even when the odd person does it never leads onto, "Okay, right, what can we do about these changes as a team?" or "How can we fight back at this as a department?"

Why don't we...? It's not that we don't care, who the hell wants to do more and more for less and less or be ripped off or have more restrictions than our children at school? It's because we don't trust each other any more and some just believe the collective fight is not their concern.

I worked with a guy and for the sake of his identity in this book I'm going to call him Rik. I worked with Rik and he is a lovely bloke and a bloody good trainer too at my old company despite the fact that being a trainer makes him think he's a little bit more senior to everyone else. It doesn't; he's a prefect at best, a milk monitor and only gets paid an extra fifty pence an hour only when he was training someone else. The thing that should have given Rik more authority at work is the fact he'd been at that company for almost twenty years. He'd worked on and mastered every single production line and tester in the place to the point where I was confident that he could build all the products blindfolded. If there was ever a problem with a build, people would go to Rik. If the supervisors needed some production knowledge, they went to Rik. If Rochelle needed advice on a part, she wouldn't go to anyone else but Rik. Yet with all this influence with the supervisors and the managers Rik had never spoken up or out about the changes, he never failed to do the overtime on offer and he never stood up for anyone around him who he clearly saw being mistreated every day. You might think it's because he was actually happy with it all and he thought it was all no big deal but he was always the first person to moan to other colleagues when the changes were rolled out or he couldn't use any grey roll. The truth of why he never spoke out comes down to a few things. Number one, despite being there nearly twenty years and regarded as the most senior member of the team he didn't believe that he had any duty or responsibility towards the treatment of his colleagues at all, just wasn't his problem. If he was coping, then that's all that mattered to him. Of course, he coped. The supervisors and Rochelle were always nicer to him because they needed his knowledge and guidance with the products. He had a better run of it than the rest of us; they wouldn't have dared raise a voice to him, they needed his knowledge. The second thing that stopped him sticking his neck out was his own feeling of security and status. Rik had spent pretty much all of his working life there, he had a reputation as the "go-to guy" in the warehouse and it was all he knew. He had no interests or hobbies other than watching a bit of football on the weekends and no kids or mortgage to worry about, on paper he didn't have a lot to lose but in reality, the job was and probably is still everything to him. At the mobility aids company, he was the top dog but anywhere else he'd have nothing, he'd feel like he was nothing. Every piece of knowledge he has is bespoke to the company he's in. If he was pushed out and forced to move on, he'd start again as a newbie and seeing the way newbies were treated at our place it's a scary prospect for someone who considers himself a face of the company. The third one is trust. I don't think he trusted anyone in that place, and I don't blame him. Staff changed over constantly, so you never really got to know anyone new for a time. The few that did manage to stay, some of them ended up being bitchy little backstabbers looking for advancement and absolutely not worthy of any trust. Bottom line, though, Rik had a responsibility as a senior member of the team to uphold the standards of the company, but it made life so much easier for him when he buried his head in the sand and pretended it was someone else's problem. A nice guy, but the fact he did nothing from his unofficial position where senior directors listened to him and paid attention to what he had to say meant he allowed evil to prevail.

The country appears now more than ever to be filled with a population only interested in themselves and nothing more. The collective cause appears to be disappearing rapidly in our society and until trust and community living comes back into the lost parts of our working class and all our lives, I really believe work life will continue to grow in a ruthless, soulless direction where we continue to grab what little money we can, rather than develop a place of personal improvement, security, the chance of fulfilment and create an environment where everybody benefits, including the business.

I'm not shocked we are behaving this way, it seems to me that we're taught to spend every waking moment of our lives looking at how we are different, how we stand out or fit in and constantly assessing our own identities. The media doesn't help with this crap either, not one bit. It seems to almost be the focus for some of these "organisations" to constantly highlight how we are different from one another. From the news to social media the focus seems to be on what divides us. Your race, the colour of your skin, country of origin, weight, size, religion, gender, sexuality, your social class, politics, Brexit or remain, your choice of a political party, your age, your level of schooling and qualifications, your position at work, the car you drive or don't, the football team you support, everything right down to the foods you eat and the clothes you wear. We take on board all of these identity checkpoints and the many more out there, add them to our list and we create little identity bubbles for ourselves. From this bubble we pick and choose who we speak to, how we speak to others and why we never really open up or bond with anyone whose bubbles don't quite resemble our own. Brexit being the most obvious example of division I can give, but I'll throw in a couple more.

No one really spoke to me at work for the first two years in the canteen at break times despite my best efforts to be polite and appear approachable and do you know why? Because I was a rugby fan, seriously, and they were all staunch football supporters to the point ninety percent of the conversation every single day was about goals, league positions, what manager was getting sacked that week and what the transfer market was going to be like, oh and fantasy football. Now I'm not having a go at football fans at all, they were all quite funny lads once I got to know them and after a couple of years, we began to open up with each other but for the first couple of years, because we had no obvious common interests there was no attempt to engage with me because they already had their own group interests and that was enough for them. They kept their conversation and reach to their own football community if you like and I kept mine to the rugby lot as a result, which was just me and my sandwich. It's totally natural to stick to what we know, and we did, until we, as a collective, could find that common ground which was boxing. Once we found that common ground we began to branch out and communicate about other things. I couldn't get into football, though, and they certainly weren't in a rush to learn about rugby despite my best efforts.

Another example, and I don't know whether it's the same in other places, but most times whenever we had someone new come into work and they were from the wider European community the first friends or relationships they tended to make were from their own country. A Portuguese worker would seek out the group of other Portuguese workers at lunch break, the Polish to the Polish group that sat together and so on. Now before anybody gets their pants or knickers in a twist over being politically incorrect about this subject, it was merely an observation I made. It didn't always happen, I'll admit, I don't want to be accused of some sort of stereotyping, but it did happen a lot more than it didn't. It wasn't because they were rude or ignorant people. It's because they wanted to seek out people they could identify with. The same language and culture, the same education or similar upbringing with emphasis on similar values, as well as going through the same experience of starting again in another country. I think it's a totally natural thing to do and if I were in their shoes, if I moved to a completely different country, hundreds of miles away from my own and in my first job in a different place where no one spoke my language, I'd look to do the same and seek out the group of English people because we'd be likely to have common ground and I would stand a stronger chance of relating to others instantly in a completely new environment. Now I'm not for a moment suggesting that anyone who does this is creating some sort of division. This last point is purely an example of how we tend to seek out what we're comfortable with, what we identify with, nothing more. The real problem are the things we choose to identify ourselves as individuals at the expense of cutting other people out that don't match our format or criteria. Then we take these identity bubbles we create for ourselves and move onto the next step which is gradually but not intentionally cut ourselves off from the rest of our peers through screen living. TV screens, laptop screens and gaming screens at home. Then we peer through car windscreens or bus windows to get to work where we stare at computer screens and then play with our phones on our break then back home in the car to more gaming and TV screens. Turning life into a neat, boxed-in existence that almost appears to be self-sustaining. To retreat socially and view life through small squares isolating us from our communities While becoming happy enough to surround ourselves with echo chambers of information and entertainment that reflect our own views and neglect everybody around us as a consequence.

We just don't talk to each other any more, not really, and when we do it's never to a degree where we always look for reason in what we're being told. Conversation is so black and white, with us or against us, matter of fact. We seem to talk at each other rather than to each other with nothing but preloaded arguments, never really taking the time to listen to anyone else unless it reflects our own views. We're losing the basic skill to hear the views and concerns of others and the ability to see reason or the other side of the coin. Everybody seems to know everything about everything! It makes me laugh because we hate the politicians when they do it, when they ignore the views of their own constituents or speak over each other in the Commons achieving what appears to be very little at times, but the reality is they are only reflecting the society they are representing. The result of constantly hearing but not listening to each other is that bonds and solid relationships are not being formed any more. People no longer communicate openly with each other, too scared their opinion could be wrong rather than listening to a different point of view, too scared to appear silly or uneducated rather than pursue the desire to become effective members of a community by looking beyond our own views. We don't trust ourselves or each other, which then leads to causes most of us could get behind like better working conditions to be lost in the struggles of individuals desperate to get their opinions across.

I see it on social media almost every day and I find it one of the most annoying things ever. Every time there's a good article or video or controversial post you can go into the comment section and I guarantee you'll find it exploding with opinions and arguments, some of them pages and pages from ops who have bitten on the message of the post or another op's comments, preaching. Despite my annoyance for it I can never resist the urge to go in occasionally and have a little scroll through some of these comments and very rarely do I ever come across people backing down from their stance or taking on board what others have said. People lock horns on these sections and post and post and post and preach and preach like they can somehow win at the game of comments! Or worse still, they think their typed-up sermon on a post that's up for five minutes until it's taken down through complaints is going to change the world and the way people think. What about the action itself? People spending hours and hours typing up pages worth of comments like it makes them more right the more they type about it. Why are you posting it? To what end? What did you hope to achieve by doing it? I just don't get it other than it's an opportunity for you to spout off how much you think you're right about something rather than taking the real opportunity to sit back and talk it out with someone in person next to you then, really listening to their views on the subject. (Long commenters, you're never going to beat the internet!)

We're creating a selfish world for ourselves and for the generations to come. The only chance of redemption is to put our swords, opinions, laptops and phones down and begin talking to the people around us once more, find out about what your family, friends and colleagues think and believe, find out what they care about and what's affecting them. Because when we do that, we learn the art of reason and understanding, we learn what it's like to be in someone else's shoes. Trust forms from the time you've invested in listening to others and when deeper friendships and relationships are made in the immediate social environments around you, you can instinctively start forming around common goals and working on them together, whether it's local community issues, the management at work or even something as big as the environment (and we all need to be thinking about this now).

We can't move forward and resolve anything that affects

all of us until we start changing how we interact with each other and how we work together and face the same issues together again. Get to know your neighbours, take up hobbies and meet new people, meet up with your mates for a bite to eat and get to know them again instead of keeping them at bay on a messaging service. Friendships and relationships take time and effort and patience, well, the real ones do anyway and they are always worth it, networks of support and great memories to be made as well as stimulating our own social wellbeing; we are social animals after all. And take your work mates for a pint or a G&T (drink responsibly) and get to know them, because until you do I'm going to have to wait for my cup of tea, book my holidays on my ten-minute break and continue taking a stopwatch to the toilet and so will your friends and family if industry is allowed to continue walking down this road.

Oh, one more thing! Let's work together to get rid of zero-hour contracts where they're not required because they're an absolute disgrace.

Thanks for reading.

Printed in Great Britain
by Amazon

67054857R00194